P9-DGZ-425

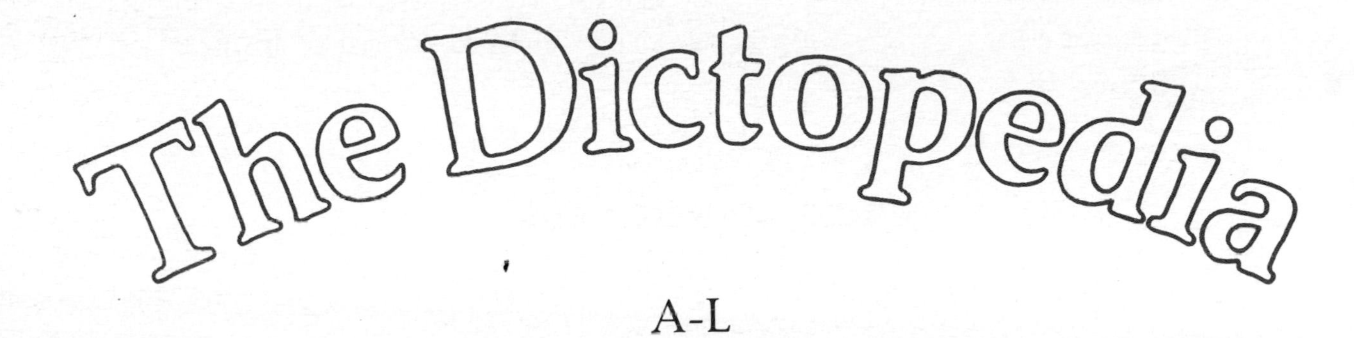

A-L

by Pleasant T. Rowland

Tonia Lapham and Lorenca Consuelo Rosal, contributing writers

Addison-Wesley Publishing Company

Menlo Park, California • Reading, Massachusetts • London • Amsterdam • Don Mills, Ontario • Sydney

ISBN 0-201-21900-X

BCDEFGHIJKL-DO-8765432

Acknowledgments

A page 6, "Aarthur the Aardvark," Lawrence K. Reilly. Page 8, copyright © 1971 by Osmond Molarsky. Freely adapted from the book *Take It Or Leave It*, published by Henry Z. Walck, Inc., a division of David McKay Co., Inc. Reprinted by permission of the publisher. Page 15, "Airplane Pilot," Jonathan Barkan. Page 19, reprinted by permission of Coward, McCann & Geoghegan, Inc. from *"I Can't" Said the Ant* by Polly Cameron. Copyright © 1961 by Polly Cameron. Page 32, adapted from "Take a Letter" from *Puzzles, Quizzes and Brainteasers* by Eileen Daly. © 1975 by Western Publishing Company, Inc. Reprinted by permission.

B page 35, "Ballet Dancer," Jonathan Barkan. Page 37, "Broke in the Basement," T. Lapham. Page 44, "Blood Brothers," Lawrence K. Reilly. Page 50, "Poor Bronto," L. Rosal. Page 52, "Bronto Loses Out," Matthew Brock. Page 54, "Buddy," T. Lapham. Page 55, "Bug," Lawrence K. Reilly.

C page 58, "Magic C," from *The Book of Magic* by Carol Lee. Paxton-Slade Publishing Corp. © 1954. Page 62, "The Capture," adapted from an episode in *The Way to Rainy Mountain* by N. Scott Momaday; © The University of New Mexico Press, 1969. Adapted and reprinted by permission of N. Scott Momaday. Page 67, adapted from *Beautiful Junk: A Story of the Watts Tower* by Jon Madian. Copyright © 1968 by Jon Madian, by permission of Little, Brown and Co. Page 73, "Caterpillars" is reprinted by permission of Charles Scribner's Sons from *Cricket in a Thicket* by Aileen Fisher. Copyright © 1963 by Aileen Fisher. Page 75 (left), "Clock," reprinted with the permission of Farrar, Straus & Giroux, Inc. from *Small Poems* by Valerie Worth. Copyright © 1972 by Valerie Worth. Page 75 (right), "Clocks," reprinted from *Talking Time* by L.B. Scott and J.J. Thompson © 1951 with permission of Webster/McGraw-Hill. Page 80, "Conversation," L. Rosal and Matthew Brock.

D page 88, "Smelly Deli Getaway," Shirleyann Costigan. Page 93, "Digging for Treasure," from *Charlie's World*, Copyright © 1972, by Lee Bennett Hopkins. Reprinted by permission of the publisher, the Bobbs-Merrill Co., Inc. Page 94, *The Hating Book* by Charlotte Zolotow. Text copyright © 1969 by Charlotte Zolotow. Reprinted by permission of Harper & Row, Publishers, Inc. Page 98, "I do not understand," from *Any Me I Want To Be* by Karla Kuskin. Copyright © 1972 by Karla Kuskin. Reprinted by permission of Harper & Row, Publishers, Inc. Page 99, "What is a good way...?" from *Jokes, Puns, and Riddles* by David Allen Clark. Copyright © 1968 by Doubleday & Company. Page 99, "Donut Bird Feeder," © 1972 by Steven Caney. Reprinted from *Toybook* by permission of Workman Publishing Company, New York. Page 100, "Dots," Matthew Brock. Page 101, "The Stranger in My Basement," Paul Stone. Page 103, "I Have a Dream," Copyright © 1963 by Martin Luther King, Jr. Reprinted by permission of Joan Daves. Page 104, "Abdul and I," Janet Bosworth.

E page 113, from *Only the Moon and Me* by Richard J. Margolis. Copyright © 1969 by Richard J. Margolis. Reprinted by permission of J.B. Lippincott, Publishers. Page 116, "Echo," Elizabeth del Valle. Page 117, "Echo," William G. Stevens II. Page 118, adapted from *Blue River* by Julian May. Copyright © 1971 by Julian May Dikty. Used by permission of Holiday House, Inc. Page 123, "I Didn't Want a Pet Egret," L. Rosal and Matthew Brock from an idea by Paul Stone. Page 126, "Elephant Joke," from *Jokes, Puns, and Riddles* by David Allen Clark. Copyright © 1968 by Doubleday & Company. Page 127, from *Perplexing Puzzles and Tantalizing Teasers*. Copyright © 1969 by Martin Gardner. Reprinted by permission of Simon & Schuster, a Division of Gulf & Western Corporation. Page 128, adaptation of the complete text from *The Checker Players* by Alan Venable. Copyright © 1973 by Alan H. Venable. Reprinted by permission of J.B. Lippincott, Publishers.

F page 142, "Standing there before the crowd . . . ," from *Only the Moon and Me* by Richard J. Margolis. Copyright © 1969 by Richard J. Margolis. Reprinted by permission of J.B. Lippincott, Publishers. Page 143, adapted from *The Boy Who Painted Wallpaper* by Mark Rubin. Copyright © 1974 by Mark Rubin. Adapted by permission of Franklin Watts, Inc. Page 149, "A feather is a letter . . . ," from *Something Special* by Beatrice Schenk de Regniers. Published by Harcourt Brace Jovanovich, Inc. Page 150, adapted from *Gleanings in Buddha-Fields* by Lafcadio Hearn. Published by Houghton Mifflin Company. Page 156, "Fire Escape," L. Rosal. Page 158, "Fish," T. Lapham. Page 164, adapted from *Letters of a Woman Homesteader* by Elinore Pruitt Stewart © 1961. Based on an incident in chapter XVI. Reprinted by permission of Houghton Mifflin Company.

G page 169, "Hoopla," L. Rosal. Page 170, "Jacks," copyright © 1968 by Kathleen Fraser. From *Stilts, Somersaults, and Headstands*. Used by permission of Atheneum Publishers. Page 170 "Stilts," T. Lapham. Page 171 "Headstand," Matthew Brock. Page 172, "Potato Vacation," © 1974 by Mary Stolz. Reprinted by permission of Roslyn Targ, Literary Agent. Page 179, "Gazpacho," Spanish translation, Rita Reilly. Page 181, "The Case of the Gingerbread Ghost," Shirleyann Costigan. Page 190. "Ginger Ale," from *Jokes, Puns and Riddles* by David Allen Clark. Copyright © 1968 by Doubleday & Company. Page 190, "Six Glasses," from *"Puzzles, Stunts, Brainteasers and Tricks" from Tell Me Why* by Arkady Leokum. Page 191, "Glowworm," from *Take Sky* by David McCord. By permission of Little, Brown and Co. Copyright © 1961, 1962 by David McCord. Page 191, "Why is it hard . . . ?" from *Jokes, Puns and Riddles* by David Allen Clark. Copyright © 1968 by Doubleday & Company. Page 192, "Grandmother," adapted from an episode in *The Way to Rainy Mountain* by N. Scott Momaday. © The University of New Mexico Press, 1969. Adapted and reprinted by permission of N. Scott Momaday and The University of New Mexico Press.

H page 198, "The Lion and the Mouse," from *The Hodgepodge Book: An Almanac of American Folklore* collected by Duncan Emrich. Text copyright © 1972 by Duncan Emrich. Reprinted by permission of Four Winds Press, a division of Scholastic Inc. Page 204, adapted from "The Clerk in the Small, Shabby Hotel," from *Puzzles, Quizzes and Brainteasers* by Eileen Daly. © 1975 by Western Publishing Company, Inc. Reprinted by permission. Page 205, "Heat," Elizabeth del Valle. Page 205, "Heavy," Steven Thomas. Page 206, adapted from the book *Juma The Little African* by John Mansfield. Copyright © 1965 by John Mansfield. Reprinted by permission of Elsevier/Nelson Books. Page 215, "Hide and Seek," T. Lapham. Page 221, "The Hummingbird," reprinted with permission of Macmillan Publishing Co., Inc. from *Toucans Two and Other Poems* by Jack Prelutsky. Copyright © 1967, 1970 by Jack Prelutsky.

I page 222, "Who Am I?" is reprinted by permission of Charles Scribner's Sons from *At the Top Of My Voice* by Felice Holman. Copyright © 1970 by Felice Holman. Page 223, "A Boat Story," from *Do a Zoomdo*, edited by Bernice Chesler, by permission of Little, Brown and Co. Copyright © 1975 by WGBH Educational Foundation. This idea was contributed by Lynn Colagiuri, Upper Montclair, New Jersey, and Catherine and Christine Gervais, Sudbury, Massachusetts. Page 226, "Incident," Marianna Beck. Page 231, adaptation of *Franklin Stein* by Ellen Raskin. Copyright © 1972 by Ellen Raskin. Used by permission of Atheneum Publishers. Page 246, "Invisible," L. Rosal. Page 249, "Island," Janet Bosworth.

J page 251, "Jack," Susan Partridge. Page 252, "Japan," Marianna Beck. Page 256, adapted from *The Genie and Joe Maloney*, © 1962 by Anita Feagles, A Young Scott Book, by permission of Children's Book Dept., Addison-Wesley Publishing Company, Inc. Page 267, "A Jackal Joke," Nancy Parsons. Page 268, adapted with permission of Macmillan Publishing Co., Inc. from *The Story of Opal* by Opal Whiteley, edited by Jane Boulton. Copyright © 1975, 1976 by Jane Boulton. Page 273, "The Kayak Paddler's Joy," from *I Breathe a New Song* edited by Richard Lewis. Copyright © 1971 by Richard Lewis.

K page 277, "Kangaroo," Shirleyann Costigan. Page 279, adapted from the book *Joey* by Wendy Kesselman and Norma Holt, published by Lawrence Hill & Company, 24 Burr Farms Road, Westport, Connecticut 06880. Copyright © 1972 by Wendy Kesselman. Page 290, "Kea," Shirleyann Costigan. Page 293, "Sky Seasoning," from *Where the Sidewalk Ends* by Shel Silverstein. Copyright © 1974 by Shel Silverstein. Reprinted by permission of Harper & Row, Publishers, Inc. Page 294,

(Acknowledgments continued on page 351)

Table of Contents

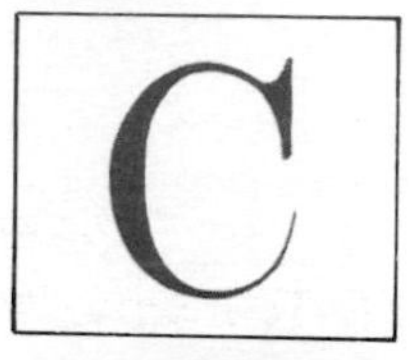

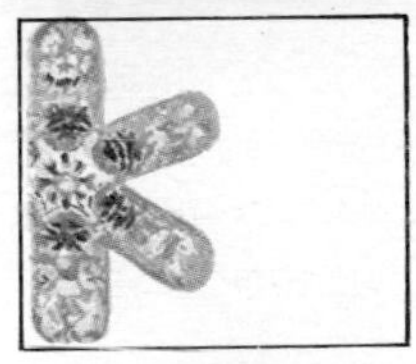

A

aardvark

The aardvark is an African animal.
Aardvark means earth pig.

Aarthur the Aardvark

Aarthur is an aardvark,
He's really not a pig.
His ears are like a donkey's.
His nose is big, big, big.

Aarthur's tongue is sticky.
It's almost as long as your arm.
On his feet are long, long claws
That keep him safe from harm.

When Aarthur's feeling hungry,
He looks for a special treat.
He uses his claws to dig the ants
He dearly loves to eat.

adventure

Take It Or Leave It

Early one bright spring morning, Jessica set out in search of adventure. The first person she met was Walter.

"I'll swap my yo-yo for your baseball cards," Jessica said. She flipped the yo-yo almost under the boy's nose. "This yo-yo is made of real boxwood. It's the best. Take it or leave it."

"Well, O.K.," Walter said.

Quick as a flash, the cards and the yo-yo changed hands.

"So long," Jessica said, starting down the street in search of adventure. She had not gone very far when she met Pendleton, on his skate scooter.

"Did you make that?" Jessica asked eagerly.

"Yup," said Pendleton.

"Want to swap it for a set of baseball cards?" asked Jessica.

"I don't think so," Pendleton said slowly.

"This is a good set," Jessica said. "Only four are missing. Take it or leave it."

"I'll take it," Pendleton said. Before he knew it, he was holding the cards. Jessica was speeding off on the scooter, in search of adventure.

Jessica covered quite a few blocks of the city on her new scooter. As she reached the park, Jessica saw a truly amazing sight. It was a girl bouncing along on a huge rubber ball. The ball had a kind of handle on top, so the girl wouldn't fall off. Jessica raced after her.

"What is that?" Jessica asked.

"It's a Kangaroo Bucking Ball," the girl said.

"Want to swap?" asked Jessica, wheeling the skate scooter around the girl. "This scooter can really move out." Jessica could tell that the girl wanted to swap.

"O.K.," the girl said.

One leap and Jessica was on the ball, bouncing away. This was really

an adventure. This was the best swapping she had ever done.

Jessica had just decided not to swap the ball for anything, when she saw a boy with a small puppy. He was dragging the puppy along and hitting it with a stick.

"Hey, don't do that!" Jessica said.

"I will if I want to. It's my puppy," said the boy. "I swapped a roller skate for it."

"He's another swapper," Jessica thought. She would have given anything in the world to have the puppy. But she knew she couldn't keep it. There was no room in the apartment. But she had to get the puppy away from that boy. He was mean!

"Have you ever ridden a Kangaroo Bucking Ball?" Jessica asked, bouncing up and down.

"No," said the boy.

"Want to try?" Jessica asked. She knew he'd like it.

"O.K.," he said. "Here–hold my dog for a minute."

Jessica patted the puppy. The puppy waggled up and licked her hand.

When the boy came back, Jessica said, "Want to swap?"

"An old ball for a dog?" the boy said. "Do you think I'm crazy?"

Jessica shrugged. She had done a lot of swapping. So she always kept something special for hard swaps. Right now it was a Japanese coin with a hole in the middle.

"I'll throw in a lucky Japanese

coin,'' she said. ''Take it or leave it.'' She started to bounce away.

''I'll take it,'' said the boy. ''Here—take the mutt.''

''Come on, puppy,'' Jessica said. ''I have to swap you to some kid who likes you and who can keep you.''

In the next hour, Jessica made a lot of swapping tries. But the kids weren't sure they could keep a dog. So Jessica wouldn't trade.

She was almost home when she saw Walter. He was still working the yo-yo, but not very well. Walter just did not have a way with yo-yos. When he saw the puppy, Walter knelt down and scratched it behind the ears.

"Would you swap the puppy for this yo-yo?" Walter asked.

"Will your Mom and Dad let you have a dog?" Jessica asked.

"They said I could have a dog for my birthday," said Walter. "Tomorrow is my birthday. Will you really swap?"

Jessica looked at the yo-yo. A dog like this was worth a dozen yo-yos. But she couldn't have a dog.

"I'll swap," said Jessica. She gave the puppy to Walter and took the yo-yo. Jessica started home, flicking the yo-yo in all directions.

"Tomorrow," she thought, "will be another day with another adventure."

airplane pilot

I'm paid to be a pilot. But even if I weren't, I'd fly just because it's fun. Like today: it was raining. I took off and climbed above the clouds out of the rain. When I saw that blue sky, I felt really good. There is nothing like flying through sunshine at 600 miles an hour.

But there are rough spots, like high winds, rain, or ice storms. I have to find the best way to get through. And that's part of the fun, too.

anaconda

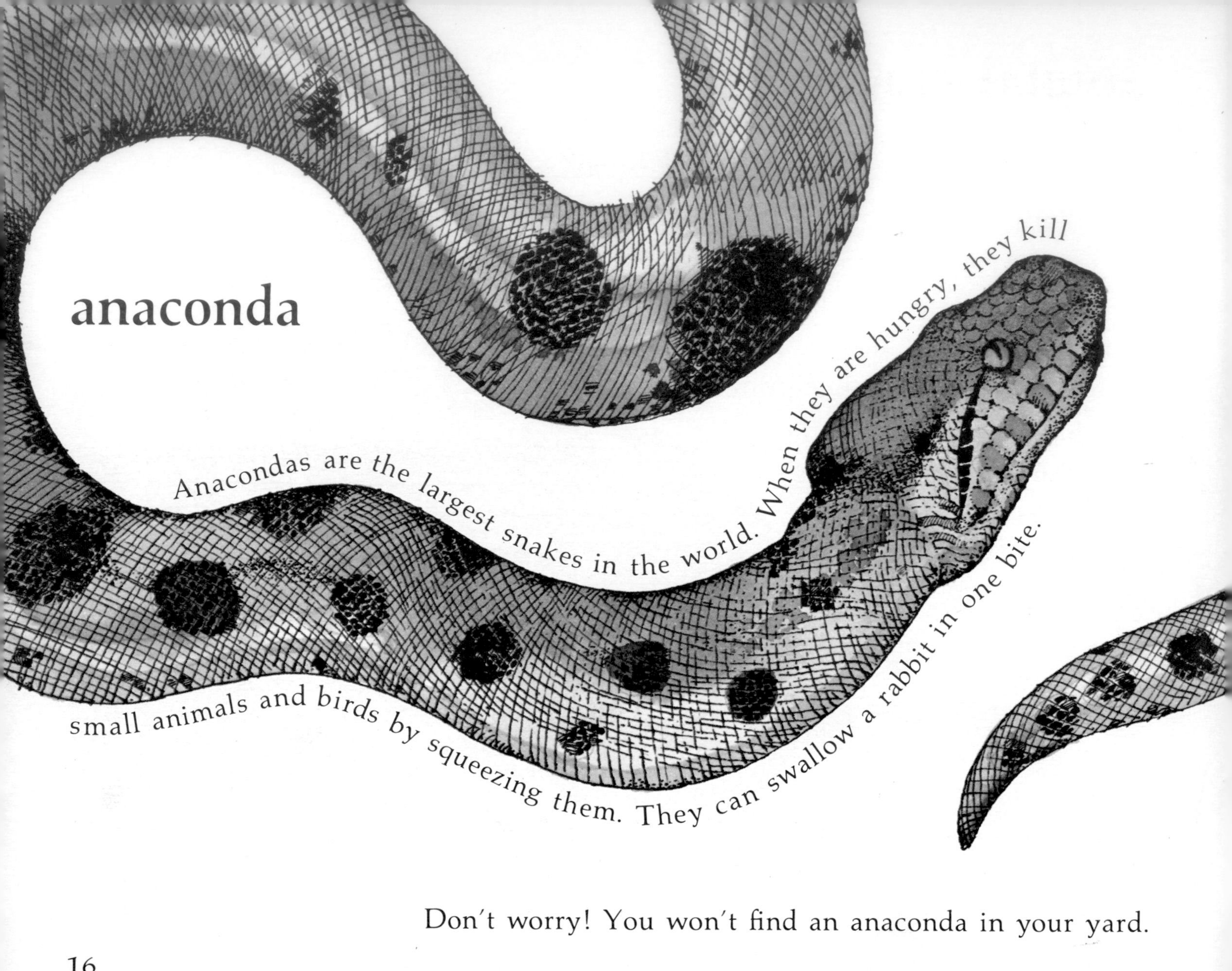

Anacondas are the largest snakes in the world. When they are hungry, they kill small animals and birds by squeezing them. They can swallow a rabbit in one bite.

Don't worry! You won't find an anaconda in your yard.

animal crackers

You may think that animal crackers
are something to eat.
They are.
But you'll crack up over
these animal jokes, so
they're called animal crackers, too.

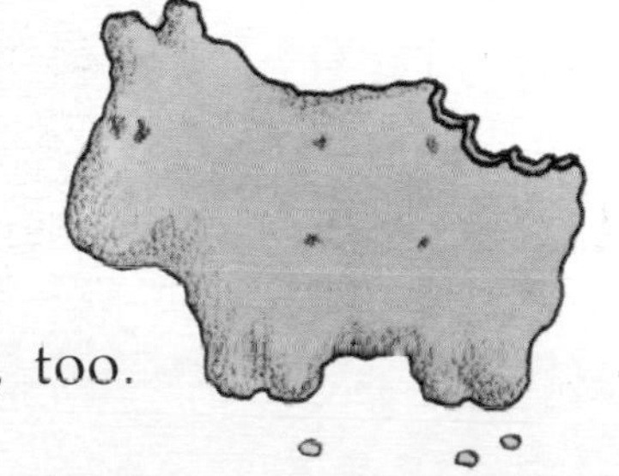

My brother is scared of monster movies. He's really chicken.

We'll have ice cream for dessert. Now don't let the cat out of the bag.

Boy, we'll need raincoats today. It's raining cats and dogs.

ant

In this story one ant can't, but many ants can—with a little help.

"I Can't," Said the Ant.

I was taking a walk
When I heard a loud clatter!
I rushed into the kitchen
To see what was the matter.

There on the floor
With the tea pouring out
Was a cracked teapot
With a broken spout.

"Good heavens! What happened,
My poor Miss Teapot?"
She rolled over and murmured,
"The tea was too hot."

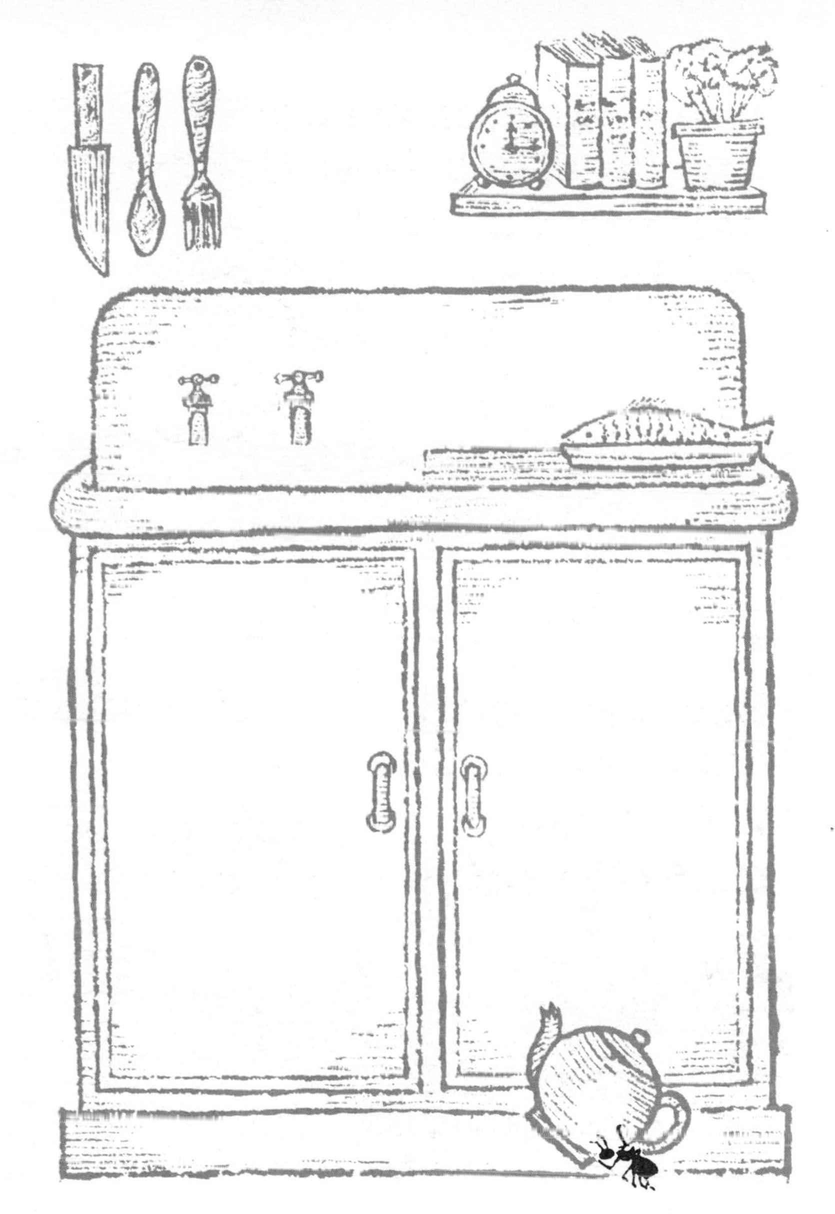

"What's all the clatter?" 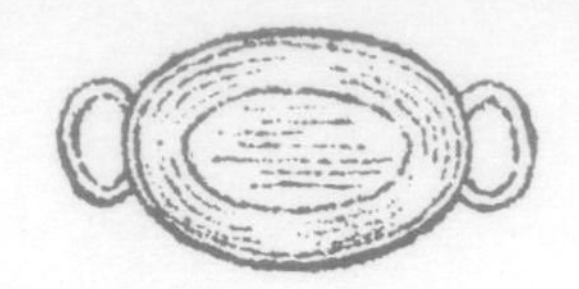 asked the platter.

"Teapot broke,"  said the artichoke.

"Is she dead?"  asked the bread.

"Just a break,"  said the steak.

"Broke her spout,"  said the trout.

"Push her up,"  said the cup.

"I can't," said the ant.

"You can,"  said the pan.

"You must,"  said the crust.

"Please try,"  said the pie.

I gathered my friends
And told them the trouble.
We spread the word
And came back on the double.

There was an army of ants
And a spider or two.
We quickly made plans
On just what to do.

"They'll mend her," 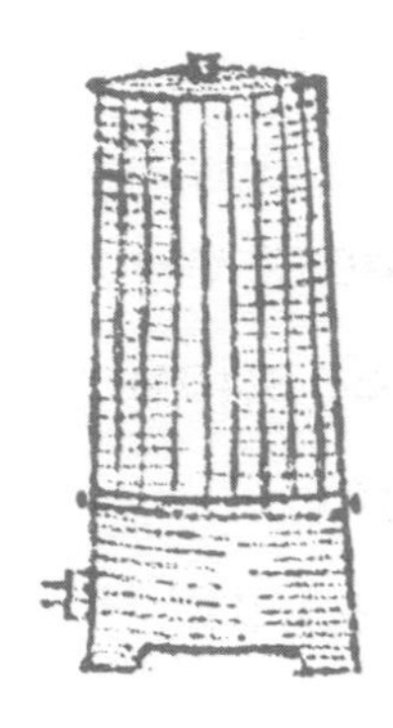 said the blender.

"They'll fix her,"  said the mixer.

"Give them time," 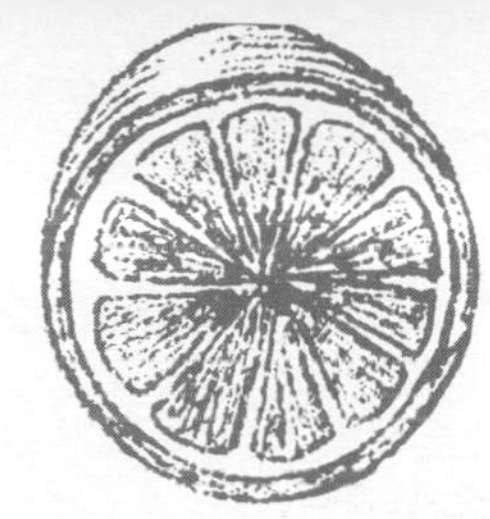 said the lime.

"Keep cool," 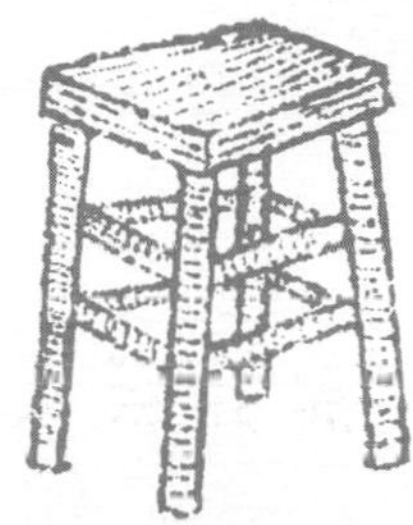 said the stool.

The spiders spun a splendid web
And wrapped it 'round her spout,
Making certain it was tight
So tea could never trickle out.

From her spout to her handle
They spun a strong string,
And when they were finished
Her spout had a sling!

"That's the ticket,"  said the cricket.

"I agree,"  said the tea.

"She'll be all right," 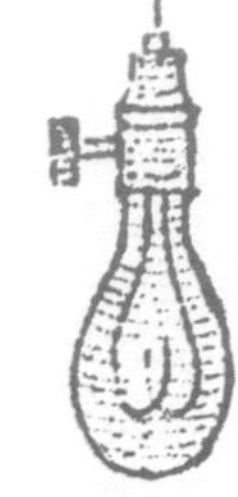 said the light.

"Gee!" said the pea.

"She's good as new,"  said the stew.

"What a blessing," said the dressing.

Miss Teapot's spout
Was nicely mended,
But we knew our job
Had not quite ended.

How do we get her
Back up on the sink?
To figure that out
We all had to think.

The spiders began
To spin and spin.
They spun up and over
And around and in.

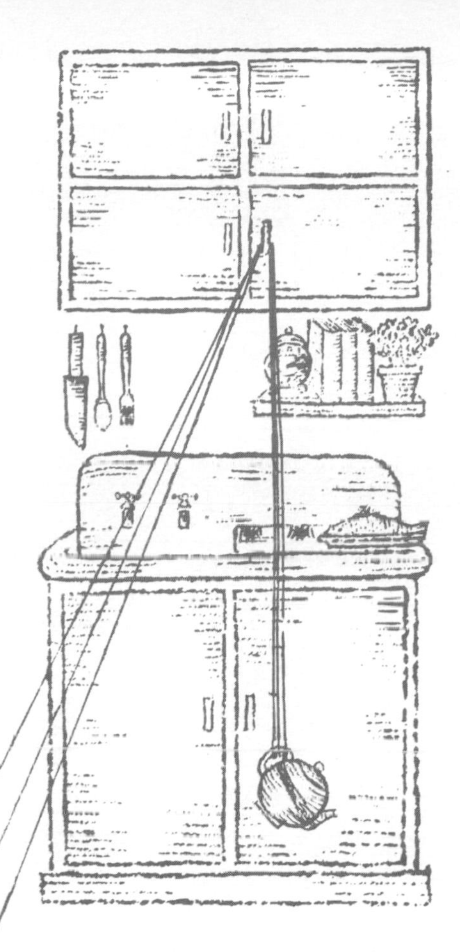

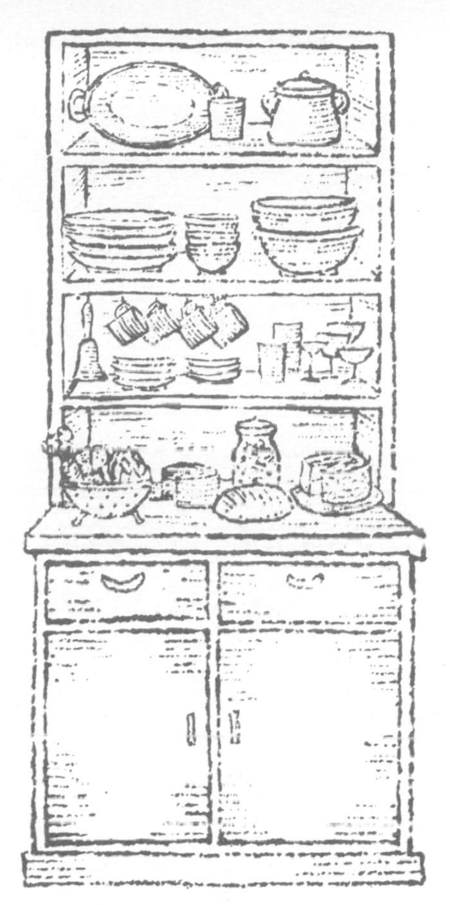

"Don't break her," 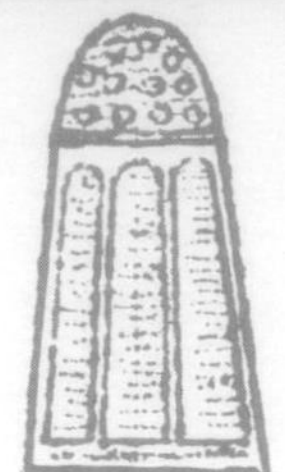 said the shaker.

"Get her up to the top,"  said the chop.

"Don't rock," 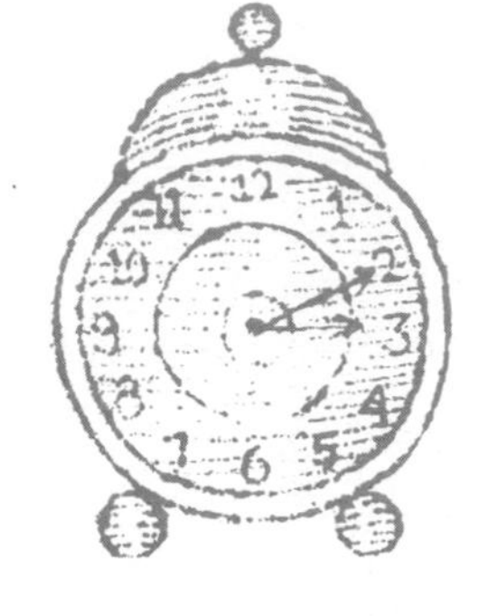 said the clock.

"I can't look," 

said the book.

"She'll crash,"  said the trash.

"A close scrape," 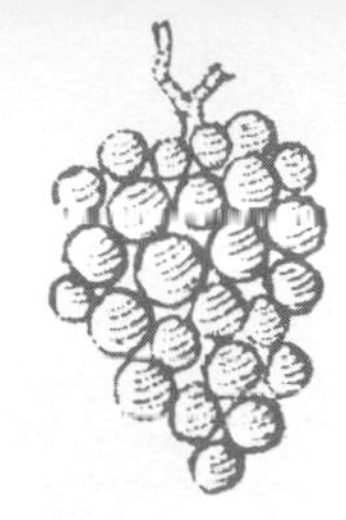 said the grape.

"What power,"  said the flower.

"We've WON!"  said the bun.

"Thank you," said Miss Teapot,
"You've been good to me.
Polly, put the kettle on.
We'll all have tea."

Polly Cameron

apology

An apology is
what you say
if you are sorry.

"I'M SORRY. OH DEAR.
HOW TERRIBLE. I DIDN'T
MEAN TO DO IT. HOW COULD
I HAVE BEEN SO CLUMSY?
IT'S REALLY THE LAST THING
I WOULD EVER WANT TO DO.
I'M SO SORRY."

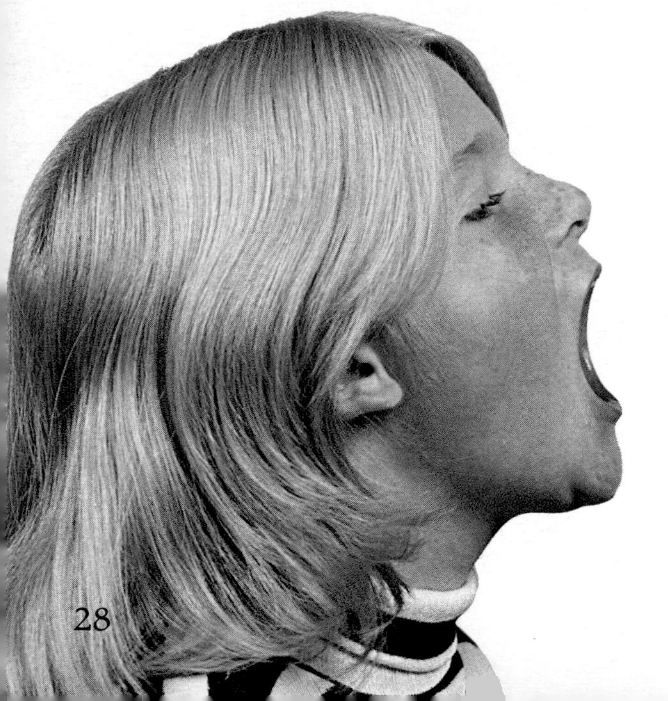

apple

Tie a string around an apple stem.
Hang the string from a door frame.
The apple should be low enough
so your mouth can reach it.
Put your hands behind your back.
Now try to take a bite out of the apple.
It's not as easy as it looks.
Try it and you'll see!

arithmetic

Joan got to the bakery just as Mr. Appleby took a pie out of the oven.

"How much for that pie, Mr. Appleby?"

"Three dollars," answered Mr. Appleby.

"I don't have that much money," Joan said. Then she started to smile.

"Mr. Appleby, how many pieces of pie do you get with four straight cuts?"

Mr. Appleby looked at Joan. "Eight."

"Well," said Joan. "If I can make more than eight pieces with four straight cuts, can I have the pie for free?"

"You certainly can," said Mr. Appleby. "But that isn't possible." Then he watched while Joan cut the pie. "You sure fooled me," said Mr. Appleby, smiling. "The pie is yours—all eleven pieces of it."

To see how Joan cut the pie, look on page 334.

armor

Armor is a metal suit. Long ago soldiers wore armor to protect themselves.

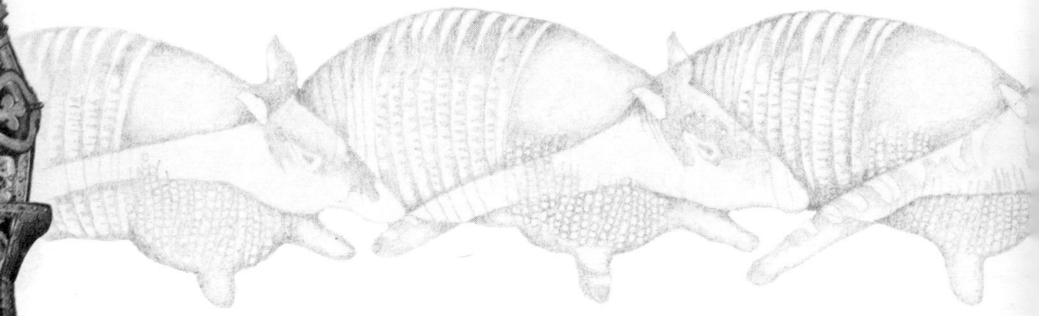

Imagine that you are wearing a suit of armor.

Is the armor noisy or quiet?
Does it feel soft or hard?
Is it heavy or light?
Do you feel cool or warm wearing it?
Is it easy to run while you're wearing armor?
Can you go to sleep in your armor?
How will you keep your armor clean?

Armadillo means "little armored thing" in Spanish.
An armadillo has a very hard shell over its body.

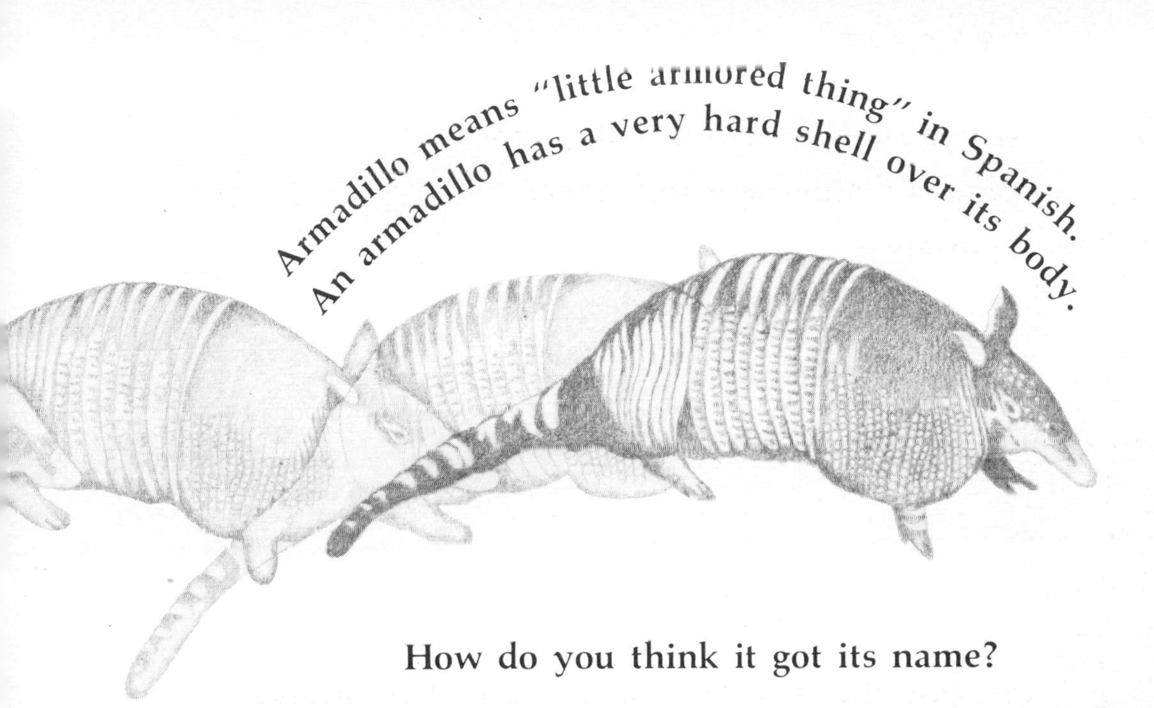

How do you think it got its name?

autograph your name written by yourself

"I'd like your autograph, Ben. Will you sign my book?" Anna asked.

"Sure," said Benjamin McGillicuddy. "But I'm going to write my name in only one letter."

"You can't do that," Anna said. "Your name has at least fifteen letters."

"It's got twenty letters," Ben said, "but I can still write my autograph in one letter."

Anna watched Benjamin put his autograph in her book.

"Why didn't I think of that?" Anna smiled.

Look at page 334 to see how Benjamin signed his autograph.

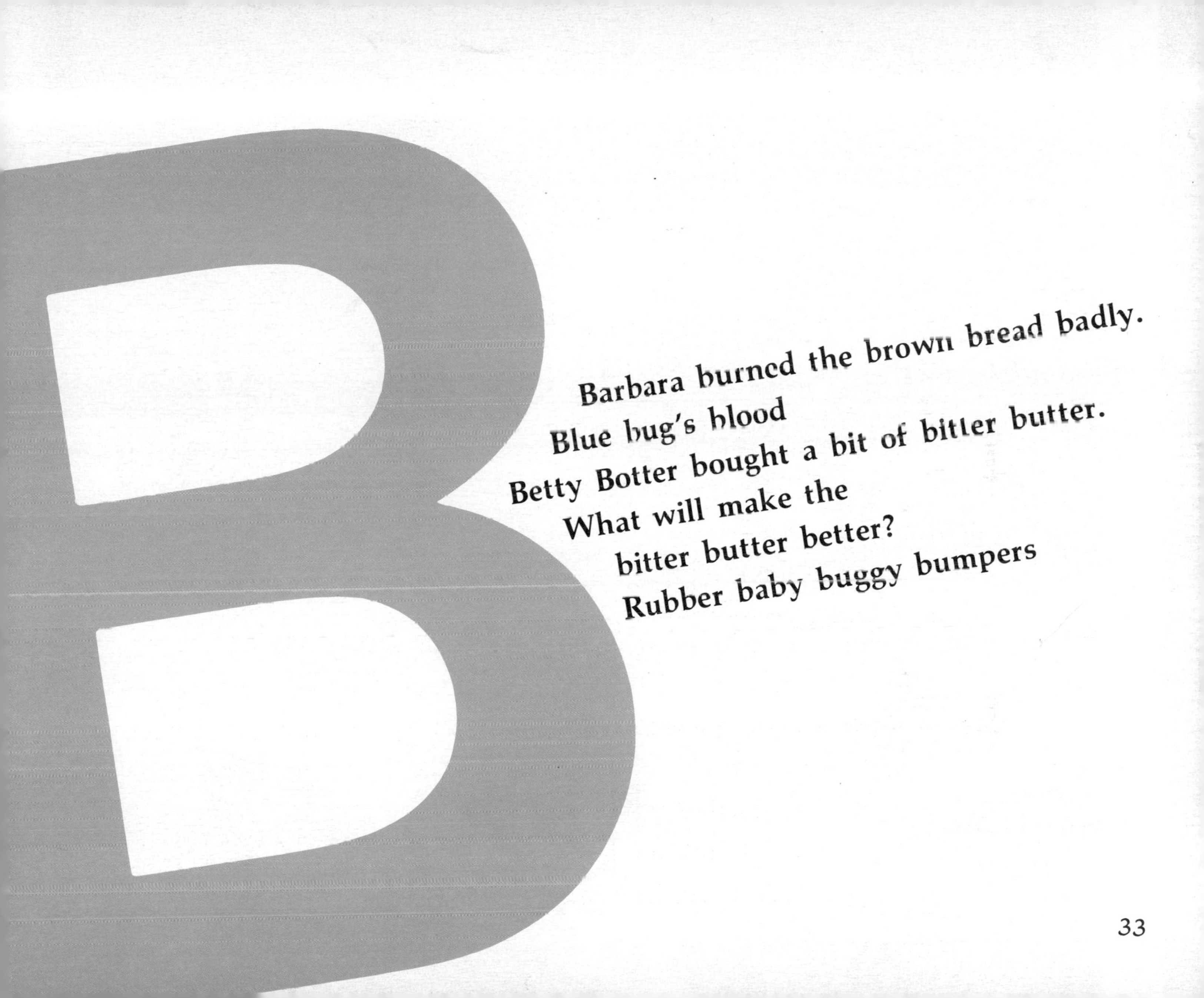

Barbara burned the brown bread badly.
Blue bug's blood
Betty Botter bought a bit of bitter butter.
What will make the
bitter butter better?
Rubber baby buggy bumpers

backwards

Here's the word *backwards* backwards:

sdrawkcab.

Try to write your name backwards.
Try to say your name backwards.
Try to drink a glass of water backwards.
Try to run backwards.

Here are some words that are spelled the same frontwards and backwards.

pup mom radar
dad sees noon

What's black and yellow and goes zzub, zzub, zzub?

A mirror will help you read the answer.

A bee flying backwards.

ballet dancer

Tony Catanzaro:

Laura started dancing when she was seven, and I started dancing in high school. We practice about six hours a day to keep in shape.

Laura Young Catanzaro:

It's great to have each part of you working just right. Every morning when I wake up, I look at my toes and say, "Good morning, toes. How are you today? And you, leg. Ready to stretch?"

baseball

I want to play baseball, but. . .

Everybody worries sometimes.

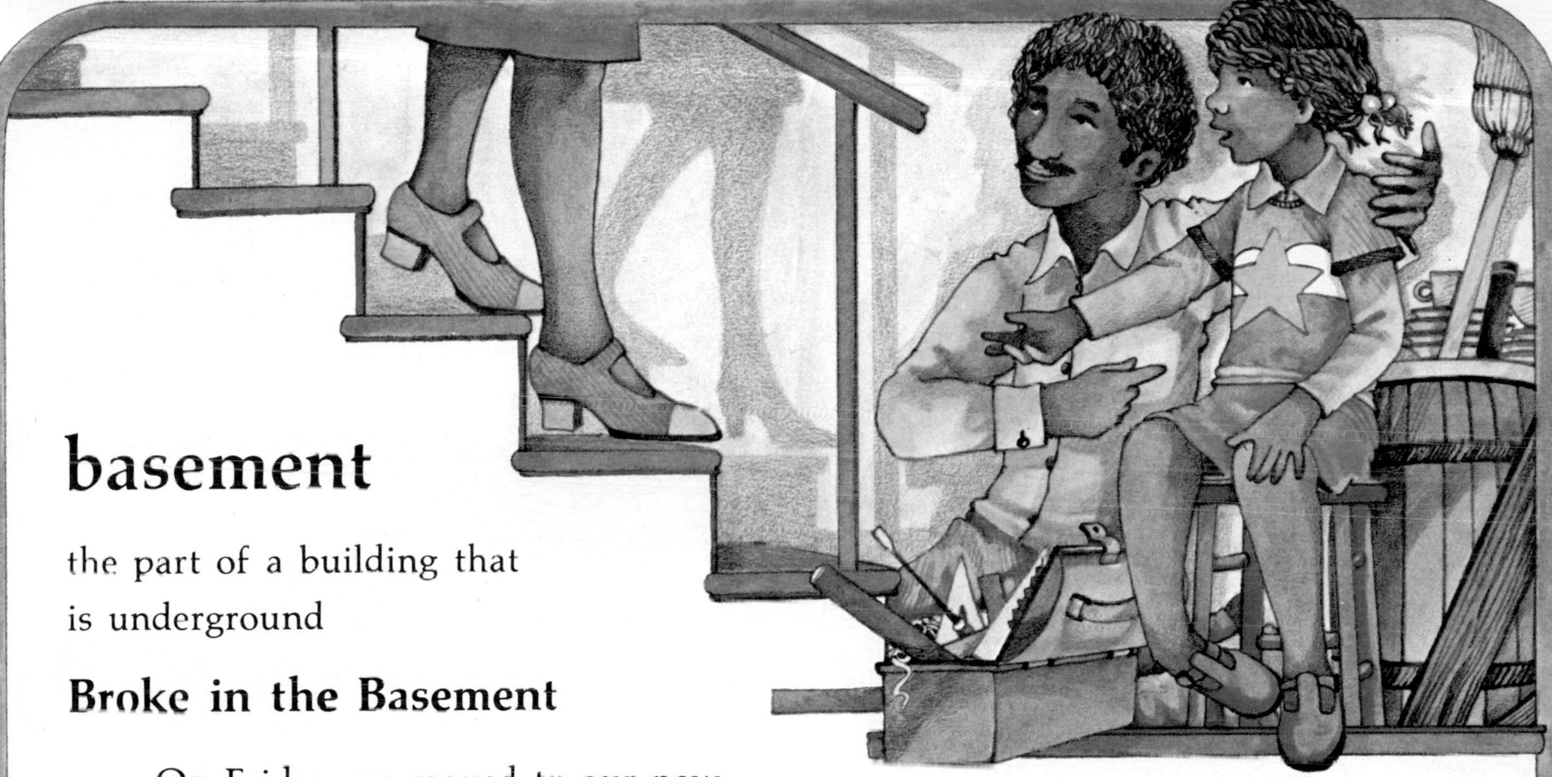

basement

the part of a building that is underground

Broke in the Basement

On Friday we moved to our new house. It wasn't really new. It needed paint, and the basement steps needed fixing. But it was a house all our own.

We were tired from moving, so we slept late on Saturday. Momma wanted to get the rest of our boxes from the old apartment. Daddy wanted to fix the basement steps.

"Can't we do both?" I asked. "I'll stay and help Daddy. Momma can get the boxes."

"O.K.," said Momma. "I'll be back by four. Then we can all go out to eat together."

"Sounds good, honey," said Daddy, "but I'm broke."

"That's all right," said Momma as she went out the door. "I have enough money for supper."

If I had known what was going to happen, I never would have let Momma go.

The basement steps didn't look bad to me, but Daddy said he wanted to make sure they were safe. I watched him for a while and then went outside.

The street was quiet. I tried to find someone to play with. Then it happened.

There was a huge crash and then a shout. I was so scared, I couldn't move at all.

"Sadie!"

When I heard Daddy call my name, I ran as fast as I could. Daddy was lying on the basement floor. One leg was bent all funny. I didn't know what to do.

"Sadie, I can't move. I think I broke my leg. Go get help."

When I got outside, I looked around. I didn't know where to go or what to do. On our old street, it would have been easy because I knew everyone in our building. I ran next door. Nobody home. I tried another house. Then I remembered the fire station! It was down the street somewhere. All I could think of was *get to the station, get to the station.*

I was out of breath when I finally got there. It took me a while to tell what had happened.

Someone called an ambulance. It seemed like a long time before it came, but I guess it wasn't.

"You'd better ride up front with us," said the driver. "You can show us where you live." When I was running there, the station had seemed miles away. But the trip home took no time at all.

Momma wasn't home yet, so while the men got Daddy into the ambulance I wrote her a note.

Dear Mom,
Meet us at
the hospital.
Love,
Sadie

Then I got into the ambulance. It seemed like a long ride to the hospital.

By the time Momma got there, Daddy's leg was in a cast.

"Are you all right?" asked Momma.

"I am now," said Daddy. "But without Sadie, I would still be lying in the basement."

"Are you sure you're all right?" asked Momma again.

"Well, I must be, honey," said Daddy, "because I'm hungry."

"Hungry?" Momma laughed. Then she gave us each a big kiss. "Do you still want to go out to eat?"

"Yes," said Daddy. "But I'm still broke."

"In more ways than one," I said.

And we all laughed.

bathtub

It is reported that Bill Wall sat in a bathtub full of water for six days. When asked how he felt, he said, "I feel like a prune."

bill

The word *bill* has many meanings:

the beak of a bird

the name of the man in the bathtub

a piece of paper that tells you how much money you have to pay

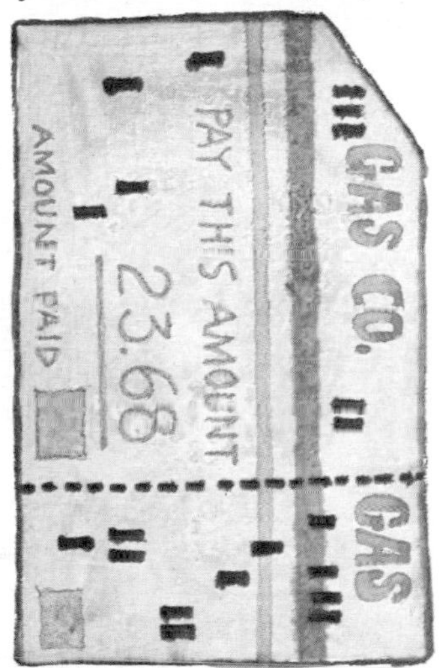

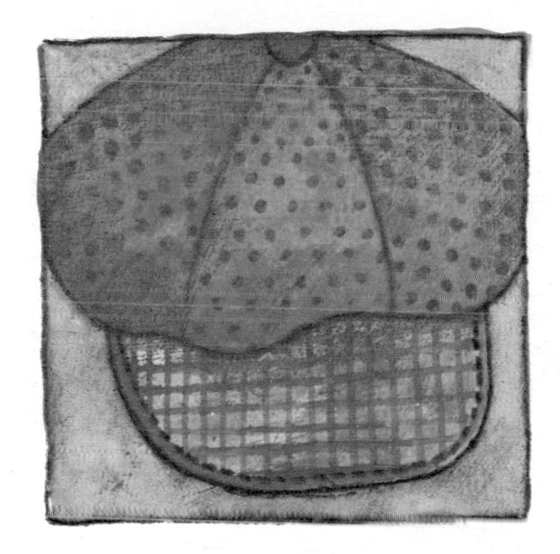

a part of a cap

a piece of paper money

blood

Blood Brothers

This story explains how blood keeps your body healthy.

Think of your body as a city. Pretend that four brothers live in your city. Let's call them the Blood Brothers. The Blood Brothers have important jobs in your city.

The first Blood Brother is a bus driver. He is called Plasma. Plasma's job is to drive the other Blood Brothers to all parts of your body.

The second Blood Brother is called Red Cells. He is the busiest passenger on the bus. Red Cells gets on and off the bus at every stop. When he gets off, he takes fresh food and air to your body. Then he picks up the garbage and gets back on the bus. He carries away the used food and air.

The third Blood Brother is a police officer. His name is White Cells. He rides the bus, too. But he does not get off at every stop. He gets off only when there is trouble. Bad Germ is a lot of trouble. If you get a cut, Bad Germ tries to get into your body. White Cells rushes off the bus to catch him. Without White Cells, Bad Germ might make you sick. But White Cells is always on the job.

The fourth Blood Brother is called Platelets. He's a plumber. He works with White Cells. When you get a cut, White Cells jumps off the bus to catch Bad Germ. Platelets jumps off the bus, too. He has to help White Cells.

Platelets stops the leak. He makes a scab over the cut to plug it up. Bad Germ cannot get back into your body.

Your body is like a busy city. The four Blood Brothers work together to keep it healthy.

brontosaurus

Long, long ago, there lived a dinosaur that looked like a great big lizard. This dinosaur was brontosaurus, which means "thunder lizard."

The brontosaurus lived in hot, wet swamps. It ate swamp plants and spent most of its time in the water.

Today there are no dinosaurs. No one knows why they all died. Maybe the weather got too hot, and the swamps dried up. Maybe the weather got too cold, and the swamps froze. Today, all that is left of the brontosaurus are giant bones.

Poor Bronto

Once a long, long time ago, Bronto was swimming in his swamp. Some of the other animals wanted to swim, too.

"No! You can't swim. You'll just have to watch," Bronto said, stomping his great, green lizard foot. SPLASH!

Every day Bronto swam around and around. He ate all the green leaves he could find. The other animals watched and grumbled.

"Why can't we swim, too?"

"Bronto spoils all the fun."

"It isn't fair!"

Now one day it got very cold. Snow began to fall.

"Brrr !" shivered Bronto. "It's too cold to swim. I know! I'll

leave the swamp and find
a better place to live."

But Bronto had eaten so many leaves that he was too big to get out of the swamp by himself. The snow started falling harder and harder.

Bronto yelled, "Help! Help! KERCHOO! Help!"

But the animals had all gone to find a warmer place to live. No one heard poor Bronto.

So Bronto sat all alone. Soon the snow was up to Bronto's knees, then to his tummy. Then it was up to his chin. The snow piled up and up and up, right to Bronto's cold little nose.

Finally, with one last kerchoo, poor Bronto died in the cold, cold swamp.

Bronto Loses Out

"No! You can't come in the swamp,"
Said Brontosaurus with a stomp.
"I want to swim alone today.
You animals can watch me play."

A great green lizard, Bronto was.
Bigger than all the rest because
He ate and ate so many leaves,
He grew as big as forty trees.

The animals were so afraid
When Bronto said, "Don't swim today,"
That in the swamp they would not go.
But they were mad at Bronto's "No!"

Where Bronto lived long, long ago,
There wasn't any cold or snow.
But one day snow fell over him
And Oh! how that did spoil his swim.

Poor Bronto was so fat and tall
He could not leave the swamp at all.
And not one friend could Bronto find
To help him leave the swamp in time.

So snow just piled up to his nose
Until alone poor Bronto froze.
And that's why there's no brontosaurus
Here today to swim before us.

brouhaha

If everyone says *brouhaha*

at the same time, there will be

a brouhaha in the classroom.

buddy

a friend

It helps to have a buddy
Who will listen to you read,
Or help with math or spelling
If that is what you need.

Have your buddy hear you read
Or listen to you spell.
Then let your buddy have a turn,
You'll find it works quite well.

Write your words and say them, too.
It's an easy way to study.
Do a little every day—
Study with your buddy!

bug

How would you like to hear someone saying, "Hey, I'm going to stomp that bug!"

Or how would you like to be crawling along, and hear a voice say, "Well, there's a good dinner!" and know it's talking about you?

Or how would you like to be flushed down the drain!

It's tough to be a bug.

People think bugs are pests. When people are being pestered, they say, "Don't bug me!" And when they don't want you around, they say, "Bug off!"

Some bugs are pests. Some bugs bite us. Some bugs eat our food. Some bugs make us sick.

But most bugs don't bother us. It's like people—a few bad bugs give all bugs a bad name. It's as if one kid was bad at recess and the whole class had to stay after. It's tough to be a bug.

Butterfly

Butterflies
dancing through
falling snow!

What a wonderful
sight it would be.

Magic

Get a sugar cube,
a pencil, and a glass of water.
Ask a buddy to write the letter
C on the sugar with a pencil.
Pick up the sugar cube and
drop it into a glass of water.
Then take your buddy's hand
and move it back and forth
over the glass three times. Say
the magic word, *abracadabra*.
The letter C has moved
from the sugar cube to
your buddy's hand!

Here's the 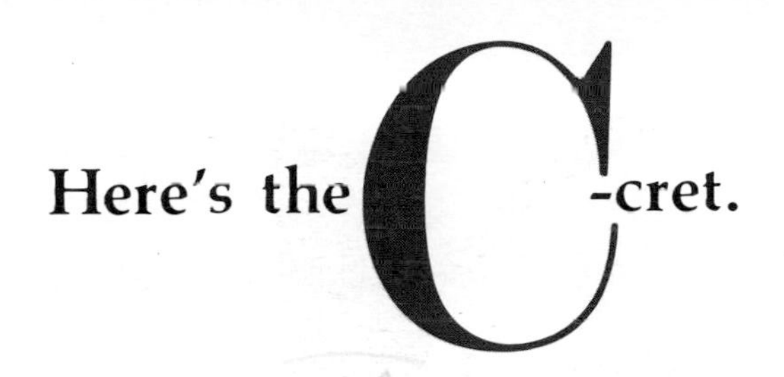 -cret.

1. Have your buddy write *C* on a sugar cube.
2. When you take the sugar cube, press hard on the letter *C* with your thumb. There is now a *C* on your thumb.
3. Drop the sugar cube into the glass of water.
4. Press your thumb on your buddy's hand as you move it over the glass and say the magic word.
5. Now the *C* is on your buddy's hand.

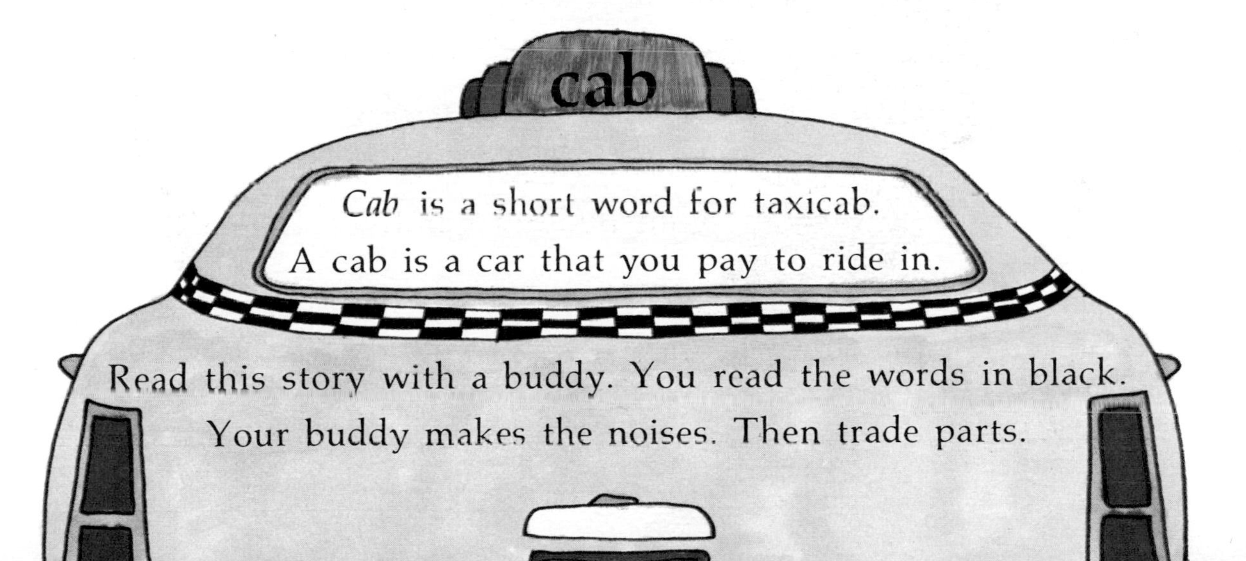

cab
Cab is a short word for taxicab.
A cab is a car that you pay to ride in.
Read this story with a buddy. You read the words in black.
Your buddy makes the noises. Then trade parts.

A cab driver HI FOLKS is sitting in the cab BEEP BEEP. The cab driver HI FOLKS is drinking orange juice SLURP SLURP. Across the street is a garbage truck GRIND GRIND. The garbage truck GRIND GRIND has a flat tire WHOOSH WHOOSH. The cab driver HI FOLKS puts down the juice SLURP SLURP. "I can fix the flat tire WHOOSH WHOOSH on the garbage truck GRIND GRIND." The cab driver HI FOLKS drinks the juice SLURP SLURP, leaves the cab BEEP BEEP, goes to the garbage truck GRIND GRIND, fixes the tire WHOOSH WHOOSH, goes back to the cab BEEP BEEP, and says,

THAT'S ALL, FOLKS!

cake
There once was a chocolate cake
Who said, "Let there be no mistake.
If you eat me too fast
Your fun will not last,
For I'll sit in your tummy and ache."

capture

to catch someone or something

The Capture

Once there was a war between two Indian tribes, the Kiowas and the Utes. The Utes captured a Kiowa named Two Hatchet. When Two Hatchet did not come back, his younger brother, Little Mountain, went to find him.

For days Little Mountain searched for the Ute camp. Finally he spotted it across the river. Little Mountain waited for dark. Then he began to swim. But as he neared the camp, dogs

began to bark and woke up the Utes. They soon found Little Mountain hiding in the grass. Before he could find his brother, Little Mountain himself was captured.

The next day Little Mountain was brought to the Ute chief. When the chief saw how young Little Mountain was, he said, "You were very brave to try to free your brother. I will make you a promise. I will put five buffalo heads in a line. The heads will have grease on them. This will make them slippery. If you can carry your brother across the five buffalo heads without falling, you may both go free."

Two Hatchet was heavy. It would be hard for his younger brother to carry him. But slowly and carefully, Little Mountain began to walk on the greased buffalo heads.

Little Mountain stepped on the first buffalo head. He thought of the day his brother showed him how to catch a rabbit.

Little Mountain stepped on the second buffalo head. He thought of the day his brother let him ride his pony.

Little Mountain stepped on the third buffalo head.

He thought of the day his brother showed him how to read animal tracks.

As Little Mountain stepped onto the fourth buffalo head, he began to slip. His brother was getting heavy. But then Little Mountain thought of the day Two Hatchet showed him how to shoot arrows while hanging onto the side of a galloping pony. And Little Mountain stepped safely on the fourth head.

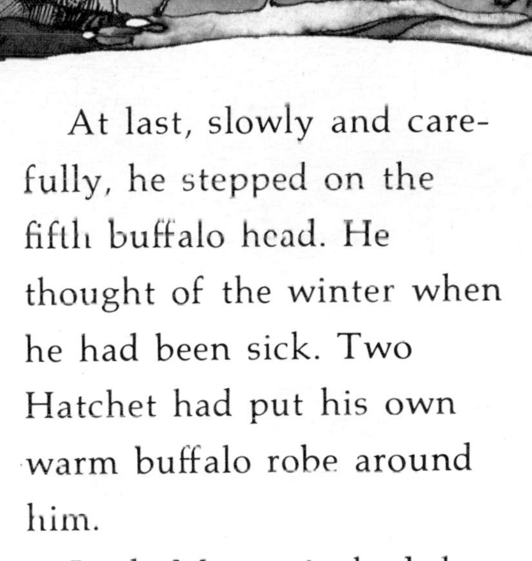

At last, slowly and carefully, he stepped on the fifth buffalo head. He thought of the winter when he had been sick. Two Hatchet had put his own warm buffalo robe around him.

Little Mountain had done it! He had walked the line of buffalo heads without falling.

The Ute chief kept his promise. He said, "You have been very brave, Little Mountain. I will give you and your brother two of my best ponies. Go. You are free to return to your people."

So the brothers were set free and went back to the Kiowa camp on horseback.

This is the way it was.

N. Scott Momaday

cartoon

A cartoon is a picture that tells a joke. Sometimes it has words, and sometimes it does not.

castle

Charlie raised a pipe over his head. "Junk! Dirty junk!" he said, smashing a bottle.

The glass broke into a hundred pieces. Charlie was so busy smashing bottles that he did not see the old man come up behind him. The man was pulling a wagon full of empty bottles.

The old man stopped. He watched Charlie. Suddenly Charlie looked up.

"What do you want?" Charlie asked angrily.

"Some bottles," said the old man in a quiet voice, "but I see you have broken them all."

The old man bent over. He looked at the pieces of glass. "May I have some of these?" he asked.

Charlie nodded. The old man carefully put the pieces of glass into a paper bag.

"Whoever heard of wanting junk?" Charlie said.

"But some of these pieces are beautiful. You broke them into fine shapes," said the old man.

Charlie laughed. "Beautiful? That glass is ugly—like everything in your wagon."

The old man looked at his wagon. Then he looked at Charlie.

"Maybe you are right," he said and walked away.

The next afternoon, Charlie saw the old man across the street. This time his wagon was full of old records.

Charlie pointed at him and shouted, "Beautiful junk! Beautiful junk!"

"It is beautiful!" said the old man, holding up a record. "Can you think of anything else that has so many perfect circles—one inside the other?" Then he turned and went on his way.

"I wonder where he takes that junk," Charlie said to himself. "Next time I'll follow him."

A few days later, Charlie saw the old man turning down an alley. Charlie followed him. He stayed far behind so he would not be seen.

The old man looked in a trash can. He found a bottle. He held it up to the sun and laughed. He put the bottle in his wagon. Then he looked in another can. After two hours, the wagon was full.

All at once, the old man disappeared around a corner. Charlie ran to be sure not to lose him.

Then—CRASH!

Charlie ran right into the old man's wagon. Junk flew everywhere.

"Why are you following me?" the old man asked sharply.

"I want to see where you take this junk," said Charlie.

"No. You might break my things."

"Then don't show me. I don't care anyway," Charlie said. But he did care.

The old man was quiet. Then he

asked, "Will you promise not to break anything?"

"I promise," Charlie said.

"Come on, then," the old man said. "It isn't far."

They walked a few more blocks.

Then Charlie saw them—three towers rising high in the air. He had never seen anything like them before. They looked like a strange fairy-tale castle.

Everywhere Charlie looked there were shapes made of cement and junk. It was a magic land. And high above it all rose the three tall towers.

"You must have worked a long time," said Charlie softly.

"More than thirty years," the old man said.

"But why?"

"Because . . ." the old man began. Then he stopped. Slowly he looked around him. He looked at all the wonderful things he had made. "Because I wanted to build something beautiful."

Charlie was quiet, thinking. Then he said, "Maybe I could help you."

"Maybe you could." The old man pointed to an empty spot. "We could build a wishing well over there."

"How does a wishing well look?" Charlie asked.

"Any way we want it to. Just bring your beautiful junk tomorrow, Charlie. We'll build it together," the old man said.

Jon Madian

Simon Rodia spent thirty-three years building his castle. The three huge towers, made from bottles and cans, shells and records, are still standing today in Watts, California. People from all over the world come to visit the castle made from beautiful junk.

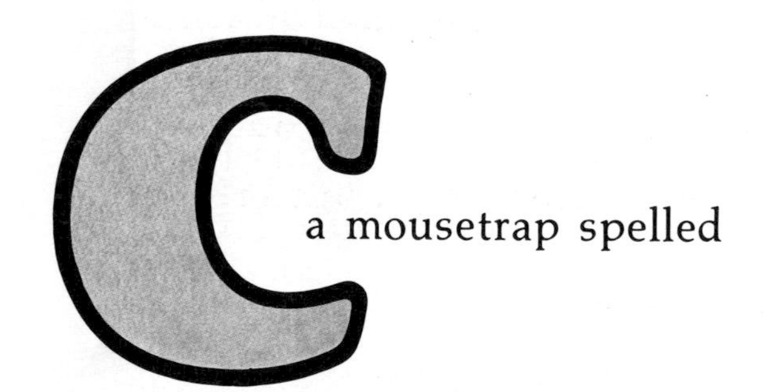

a mousetrap spelled

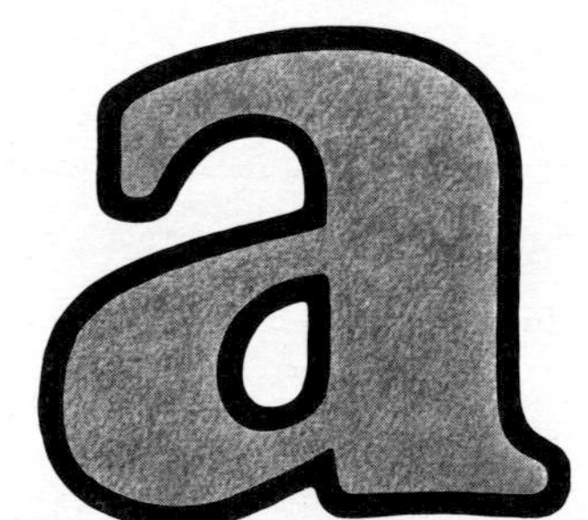

with three letters

caterpillar

A caterpillar looks like a worm. Caterpillars turn into butterflies or moths.

Caterpillars

What do caterpillars do?
Nothing much but chew and chew.

What do caterpillars know?
Nothing much but how to grow.

They just eat what by and by
will make them be a butterfly.

But that is more than I can do
however much I chew and chew.

Aileen Fisher

chair
something with legs that can't walk
and a seat that can't sit down
What has two hands, but no arms?
a clock
What has a head and a foot, but no body?
a bed
What has four legs, no back, and never walks?
a table

clock

This clock
Has stopped,
Some gear
Or spring
Gone wrong–
Too tight,
Or cracked,
Or choked
With dust;
A year
Has passed
Since last
It said
Ting ting
Or tick
Or tock.
Poor
Clock.

Valerie Worth

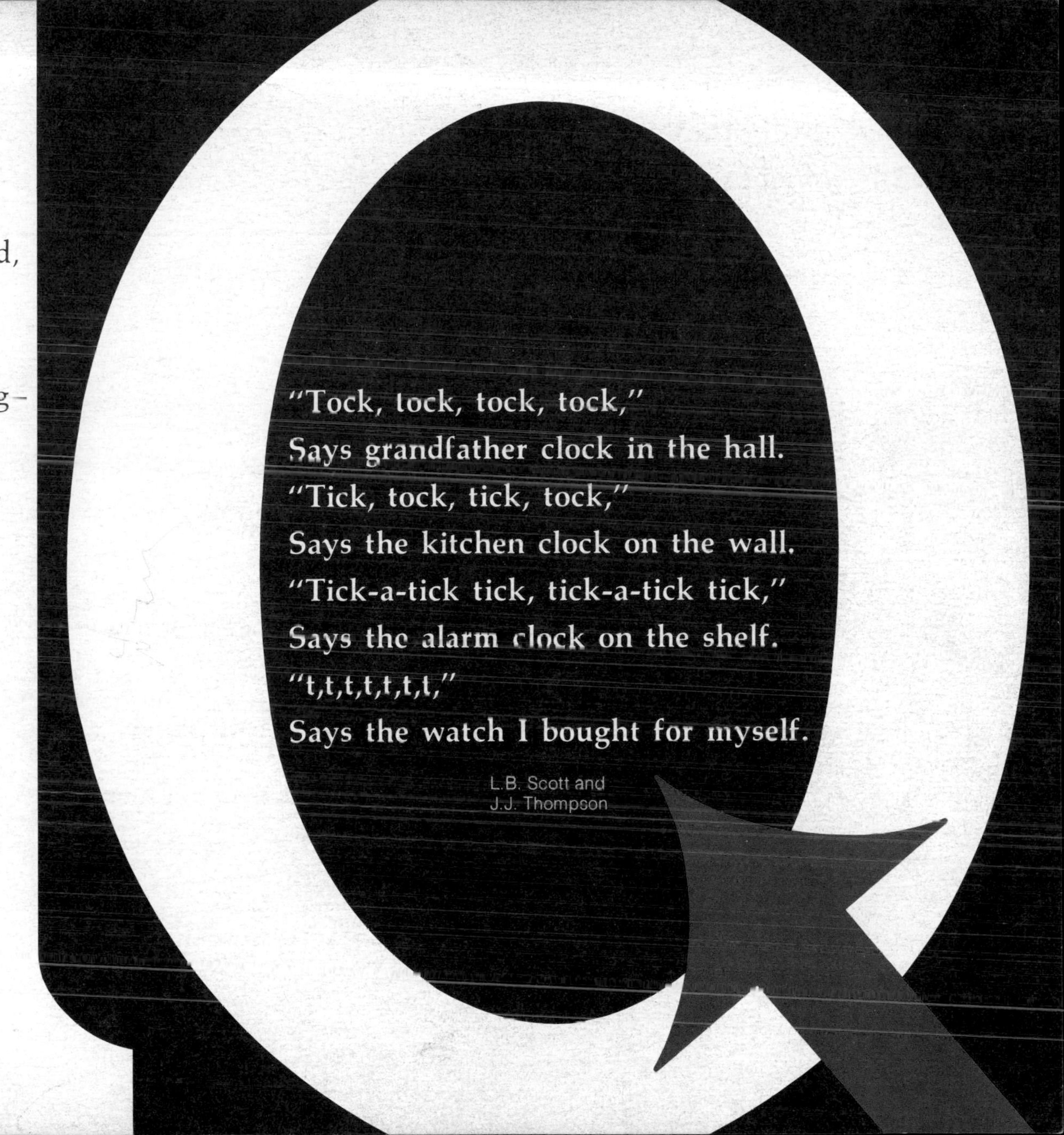

"Tock, tock, tock, tock,"
Says grandfather clock in the hall.
"Tick, tock, tick, tock,"
Says the kitchen clock on the wall.
"Tick-a-tick tick, tick-a-tick tick,"
Says the alarm clock on the shelf.
"t,t,t,t,t,t,t,"
Says the watch I bought for myself.
L.B. Scott and
J.J. Thompson

clothes

There was once an emperor who loved clothes. He loved clothes more than anything else in the world. He had whole rooms full of clothes. He had a room just for his crowns. He had a room piled high with shoes. And he had room after room full of nothing but robes. There were long robes and short robes, fur robes and cloth robes. Yes, the emperor loved clothes. And he knew that his clothes were the most beautiful in the land.

One day the emperor looked out his window and saw two men on the street below. His eyes almost popped out of his head. The two men were wearing the most beautiful clothes the emperor had ever seen. Their hats had so many feathers that no one could count them. Their robes had so many ruffles that they made the emperor quite dizzy. And their shoes were so shiny that they hurt the emperor's eyes. This, of course, made the emperor mad. In fact, he was furious.

"Come here at once," he shouted. "Who are you? And how dare you have better clothes than the emperor?"

It was true. Their clothes were more beautiful than the emperor's.

"Nobody can look better than the emperor. It's not right. It's not allowed," cried the emperor.

"Now, now," said the two men. "Don't worry. We can make you the finest clothes in the land. Just sit down quietly and listen to us."

And as the emperor listened, he started to smile. Soon he was laughing.

"What a wonderful idea! You will make clothes for me. But only the smartest people in the land will see my clothes. The stupid people will see nothing. My clothes will be the most beautiful in the land. And only the smartest people will see them. Go! Begin at once."

The two men started to make the emperor's clothes. At least that's what the emperor thought they were doing. But really they were just pretending. They pretended to measure. They pretended to cut with their scissors. They pretended to sew the cloth.

People came to look. They couldn't see anything. But they said, "How lovely, how fine." Nobody dared to say that there was nothing to see, because nobody wanted to look stupid.

At last the men were finished. The emperor was so excited that he ordered a parade. He wanted to show off his new clothes.

When the two men came to show the emperor the new clothes, the emperor didn't know what to say. He couldn't say that the clothes were beautiful because he couldn't see any clothes at all. So he didn't say a word. He pretended to put on the new shirt, the new shoes, and the new robe. He couldn't feel anything. He couldn't see anything. And still he didn't dare say anything.

The parade was perfect. Everyone cheered and clapped because everyone wanted to look smart. That is, everyone cheered except two children.

They started to laugh. Then they started to shout.

"Look! Look at the emperor! He doesn't have any clothes on."

Soon everybody was laughing. There was the emperor without any clothes. Even the emperor knew that he had been fooled. He knew that what the children said was true. But he just kept on walking, nude as a noodle.

comb

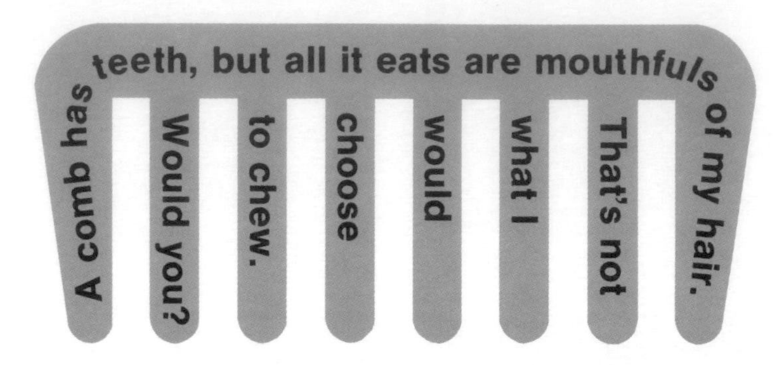

A comb has teeth, but all it eats are mouthfuls of my hair.
Would you?
to chew.
choose
would
what I
That's not

conversation

When people talk together, they are having a conversation.

Pick a buddy. You read the words written in green. Let your buddy read the ones written in red. Make your reading sound like talking.

Hi, Frankie. Did you hear what happened?

You mean about the circus?

Yes. The police have looked all over town, but they can't find it.

But how could a circus get lost?

Didn't you hear? It's not lost. It's been stolen!

Stolen! You must be kidding! How do they know it's been stolen?

Well, the police went to the circus grounds, but no one was there. All they found was HELPP written in popcorn near the lion cage.

You know, Tony, there's only one person who would be crummy enough to steal the circus.

You mean . . .

Right. Mean Captain Crumb.

He must be hiding the circus somewhere. If only we could figure out where. I know, how about the woods?

No, that would never work.

Why not?

Because the elephants would get stuck between the trees. But maybe mean Captain Crumb hid the circus on the island in the lake.

No. The island has already been checked. The police roared around the island on their motorcycles, but no lions roared back. So, I guess the circus couldn't be there.

Maybe it's in the swamp. The prickly bushes would make a great hiding place.

No, that would never work. Captain Crumb couldn't hide the bears in there. The prickles would hurt their bare feet. But how about the graveyard?

No. Everyone knows that mean Captain Crumb is afraid of ghosts. Tony, where could the circus be?

Wait a minute, Frankie. We forgot the most important thing!

What's that?

Whoever wrote HELPP in popcorn spelled it with two P's! Don't you see? Two P's? That's it!

That's what? Two P's? Popcorn? What are you talking about?

I know where the circus is. Can't you figure it out?

This bird is a crane.

Why is this machine
called a crane?

cuddle
snuggle
hug

Daisies

Daisies are the day's eyes.

deaf

A deaf person cannot hear.

Rosanne Landolfi wrote this poem when she was in the sixth grade. It is about her four year-old sister, Diane, who is deaf and has not learned to talk.

Diane

I take her by her little hand,
Up to the shore to play in the sand.
Her dog pushes her to the ground.
She doesn't hear a single sound.
"Look at the seagulls," she seems to say,
"See how they fly—far, far away."
When she goes home, there is a tear.
Oh, what I'd give if she could hear!

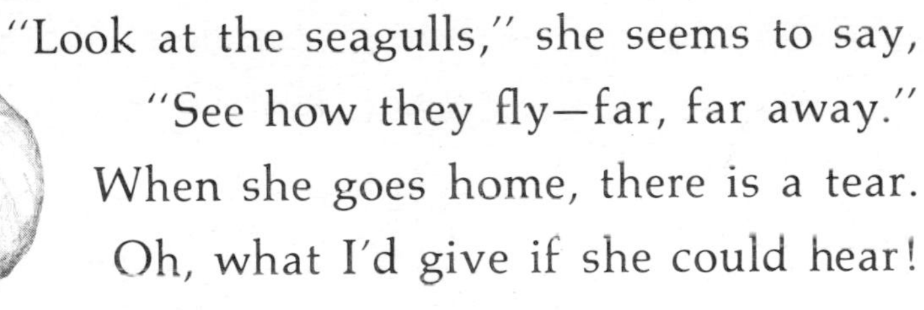

delicatessen

a store that sells food
that is ready to eat
Sometimes it is called a deli.

The Smelly Deli Getaway

We were standing outside Mr. Supperfine's delicatessen, looking at all the food in the window. Sara and Wendell liked the long salami best. I thought ham and cheese would taste better for lunch. We were trying to make up our minds when we saw the man come out of the deli. He carried a big deli-box in each hand. He crossed the street, and lickety-split he was out of sight.

"P.U.!" said Wendell. "What's that smell?"

"That's pickled pigs' feet," said Sara. "At home we have it for lunch every Saturday."

"Give it back to the pigs," said Wendell. "It stinks."

"It tastes good," said Sara. "Funny, Mr. Supperfine didn't put those boxes into a bag. That man has dripped pig juice all down the street."

"Let's go ask Mr. Supperfine to be more careful," said Wendell, "or else he'll stink up the whole town."

We went into the store.

"Nobody's here," said Wendell.

"What's all that banging?" asked Sara. We all listened.

"I think it's coming from the meat refrigerator," I said. "Maybe it's the hot dogs. They're cold, and they want to get out."

"That's not funny," said Wendell. "Somebody's locked in there."

I pulled and pulled on the heavy refrigerator door. Finally it swung open. Out popped Sara's mother, blue-cold.

"Mom!" yelled Sara. "What were you doing in there?"

Behind her came Mr. Supperfine. "C-c-call the p-p-police," he chattered. "F-f-fast! I've been robbed!"

"Was it the pigs'-feet man?" Wendell asked.

"Yes," said Mr. Supperfine. "He pointed a gun at me. Then he asked for all my money. I was so scared that I put it in the first thing I could find—some boxes of pickled pigs' feet. Then he put us in the first thing he could find—the meat refrigerator. Now how

will I ever get all my money back?"

"We'll go and smell it out," said Wendell.

We left the store. Mr. Supperfine was calling the police.

A half-hour later we called the delicatessen.

"Come to 10 River Street," Wendell said. "The pig juice stops here. We think the robber must be inside. And hurry! The smell hurts my head."

When the police came, we were standing outside the house, feeling very important. They went in and brought out the robber and the pickled money. The robber was glad to go. He was just that sick of smelling pickled pigs' feet.

"I know how he feels," Wendell said, wrinkling his nose.

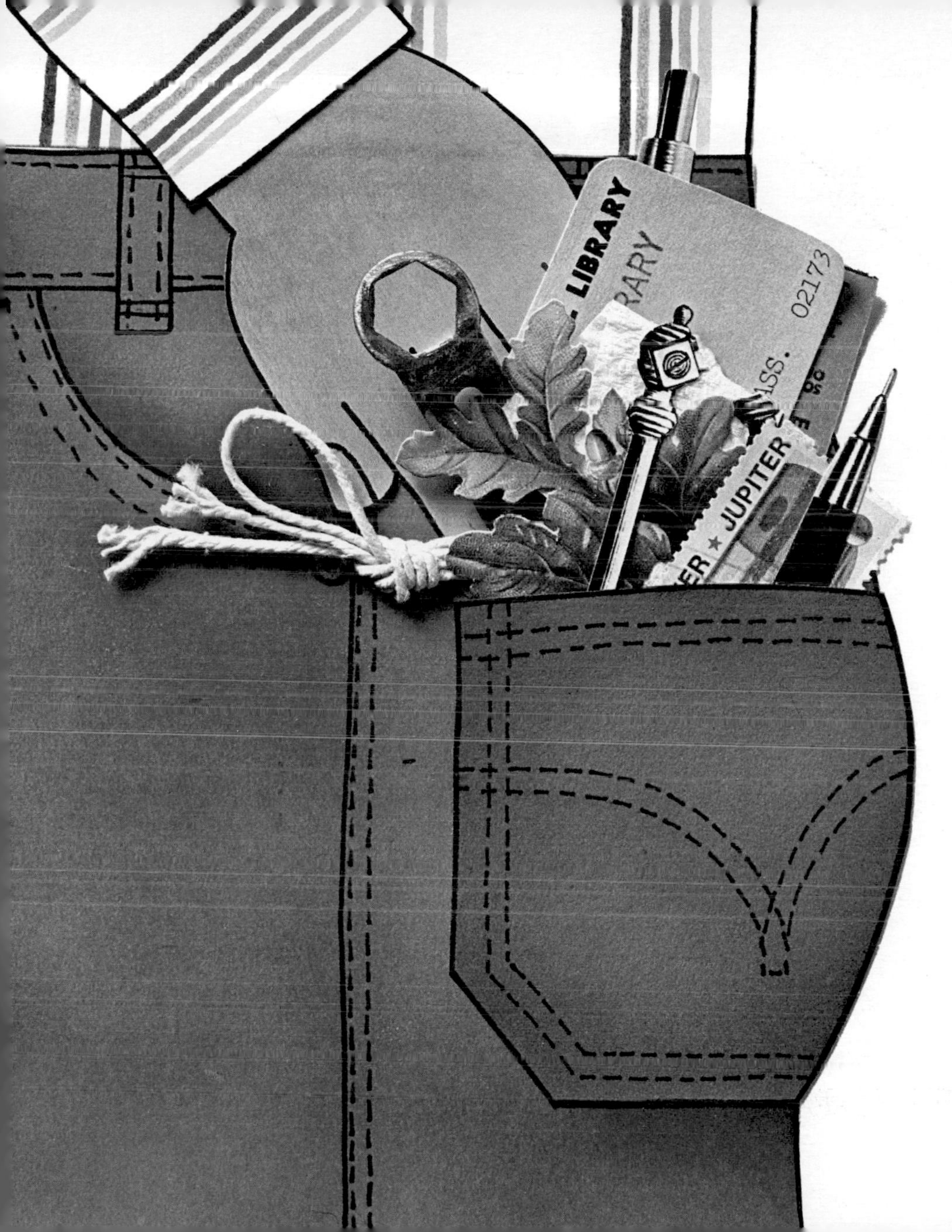

dig

Digging for Treasure

I put my hand in
and found—

a rusty skate key,
a part of a tool,
a dead bee I was saving
to take into school;
my library card
and
a small model rocket.

I guess it is time
to clean out
my pocket.

Lee Bennett Hopkins

discuss

to talk about something

This story shows how a little problem can become a big problem if you don't discuss it.

I hate hate hated my friend.

When I moved over in the school bus,
she sat somewhere else.
When her point broke in arithmetic
and I passed her my pencil,
she took Peter's instead.

"Ask her," my mother said,
"ask your friend why."

But I wouldn't,
I couldn't,
I'd rather die.

What if she should say
Oh, please, just go away.
You're ugly and dumb.
Being with you
was never fun.

Oh, I hated my friend.

When it was her turn to wash the board,
she didn't ask me to help.
When it was time to choose teams,
she didn't choose me.
And when I made a basket
and everyone else yelled YAAAA,
she turned away.

Oh, I hated my friend.

When I went to walk home with her,
she had already gone.

When she took her dog out
and I whistled to him,
she put him on a leash
and led him away.

Oh, I hated my friend.

"Ask her," my mother said,
"ask her why."

I couldn't,
I'd rather die.
No—
if that's the way she's going to be,
it's quite okay with me.

"Ask her," my mother said,
"ask and see . . ."

I wouldn't,
I couldn't.
But
maybe . . .

"You've been so rotten," I said.
"Why?"

She looked as though she'd cry.
"It's you," she said. "Last week
when I wore my new dress,
Sue said Jane said you said
I looked like a freak."

"I did not!
I said you looked *neat*!"

She looked straight at me for a while,
and then we both began to smile.
My friend said, "Hey,
maybe tomorrow we can play?"
"Oh, yes," I said, "OKAY!"

I didn't hate her anyway.
I wish it were tomorrow.

Charlotte Zolotow

dog

I do not understand
ARF
How people
ARF
GROWL
BARK
Can walk around on two
ARF
Legs.
I see them in the park
BARK
And all around the town.
They walk around on just two legs
Without
BARK
Falling down!
ARF

Karla Kuskin

donut

a hole with a little round cake around it

You can make a bird feeder with a donut, two plastic lids, and some string. Make sure you tie a big knot so the string won't slip through.

dots

Dots in your eyes
when you shut them tight
All suns and lights and yellow bright balls
floating floating
Across black lids
Where night should be
Where daydream is
Just pots of spots and polka dots
Big colored holes: all blue and red and waiting
For closed eyes.

Dracula

Dracula is a make-believe monster in the movies and on TV.

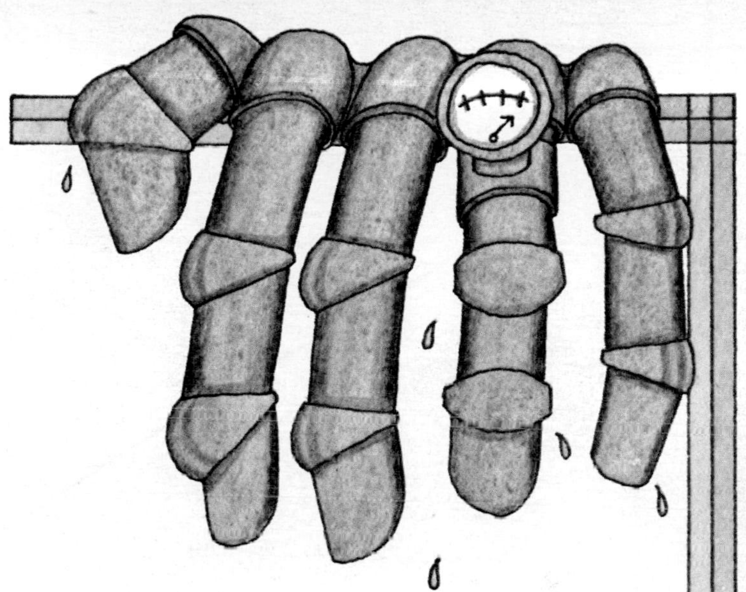

The Stranger in My Basement

I have a problem.
There is someone in my basement.
I can hear him pounding.
I know who it is, too.
It's Dracula.
I know it's Dracula because
I saw him on TV last night.
He always makes awful noises.
I'm scared.
I wish my sister would get
home from high school.
I wonder why she's late.

There he goes again.
He's pounding again.
It's getting louder.
He wants to get out.
If he gets out, he will come up here.
Where is my sister?
She's never late like this.
Maybe Dracula got her.
I can hear footsteps.
Here he comes. He's at the door.

"Hey, Steve, sorry I'm late. The bus broke down, so I had to wait. What's that noise in the basement? I bet it's that monster of a furnace."

dream

A dream can be two things:

1. something you feel, see, or think about while you sleep
2. a wish or hope

I have a dream today.
I have a dream that one day . . .
little black boys and black girls
will be able to join hands with
little white boys and white girls
and walk together as sisters and
brothers.
I have a dream today.

dromedary

A dromedary is a camel that has only one hump. Dromedaries are often used for riding because they move faster than other camels.

Abdul and I

I'll introduce myself. My name is Yasmine, and I am a dromedary. Please don't call me a camel. Ordinary camels have two humps. They are not as nice-looking as dromedaries.

I am not just any old dromedary, either. I belong to Princess Shahran. She has other dromedaries. But she likes me best. How do I know? Because she rides me most often. When she wants to go for long trips across the desert, she always asks for me. "Please saddle Yasmine," she says. That makes me feel good.

It is true that I don't like to kneel down to be saddled. Sometimes I grumble a little. But I do have

long legs, and it takes a while to bend them. The princess understands. She always waits for me.

Then off we go across the burning sands. We visit the princess's relatives. They live far and wide across the desert. Sometimes we ride for two or three days before we get to a village. Princess Shahran loves these trips with me, and I love being her favorite dromedary.

One day everything in my life changed. A horse arrived.

"Well, camels, out you go," the horse said. "Princess Shahran won't need you any more. I am Abdul. I can run faster than you can, and I am surely more handsome."

I thought that he was very rude. I told him so. "We are not just camels," I said. "We are dromedaries. Please call us that. And you may go faster, but that's all. What good does that do you in the desert? You can never take the place of a dromedary. Our woolly coats keep us from sweating, and we can go for weeks without water."

"Oh, close your mouth," said Abdul. "I'm tired of you. Who cares if you can go without water? Who cares if you don't sweat? I can run as fast as the wind. And even better—I never get lost."

I had never heard such words in my life. I was so angry, I started hissing and sputtering.

"Listen to that," Abdul said. "You are just as bad-tempered as all the camels I know. I can't believe anyone ever rides you."

"I'm a dromedary," I said weakly. Then I turned around, as if I didn't care what he said.

Well, I did care. That night was the worst night of my life. Abdul just stood there and swished his tail. Whenever he made a sound, someone brought him food. Whenever he shook his head, someone came running. No one came to look at us dromedaries. Oh, were my feelings hurt!

The next morning Princess Shahran was ready early. "Saddle Abdul for me," she said. My heart sank. I could not believe it.

The princess and Abdul were gone for only one day. Abdul's legs were tired when he got back. But as soon as he had some rest and food, he started boasting. "What a day!" he said. "The princess and I just sailed across the desert. She said I was such fun. I can't wait for tomorrow. And how, dear camel, are you?"

"*Dromedary* is the word," I said. "*Dromedary.*" But I was too tired and unhappy to fight with Abdul any longer.

The next morning

Princess Shahran said, "Saddle Abdul for me."

And again on the next morning.

This went on for days. It wasn't only my pride that was hurt. I truly missed the princess. I missed the desert wind and the hot sun.

Then one morning the two of them set out for a faraway village. They did not return that afternoon. They did not come back that night. The king was very worried when he heard the news.

On the next morning, the king had all the

dromedaries saddled. Off we went to look for Abdul and Princess Shahran. We walked and walked and walked in the blazing sun. It didn't bother us at all. We were proud to be traveling with the king.

At last we found them. They were way out in the middle of nowhere, just sitting there in the desert. Princess Shahran looked very, very tired. And Abdul did not look at all well.

"What happened?" the king asked. "I was afraid that I would never see you again."

"Abdul collapsed, Father," Princess Shahran replied. "I forgot that he is a horse and needs more water than Yasmine and the other dromedaries."

I loved hearing those words. I got down on my knees and didn't grumble at all.

"Oh, Yasmine!" said the princess. "I am so glad to see you." She climbed onto my back, and I stood up again.

I looked over at Abdul. He got to his feet ever so slowly. Then he said, "You win, dromedary."

It took us two days to get back because we had to wait for Abdul. He walked very slowly.

After a few weeks, Abdul felt better. He apologized for being rude. Also, he did not call us "camels" anymore. He was careful to say "dromedaries." We all became great friends.

Everything is fine now. Princess Shahran rides Abdul when she wants to get somewhere quickly. But when she wants to visit friends in faraway villages, she says, "Saddle Yasmine for me."

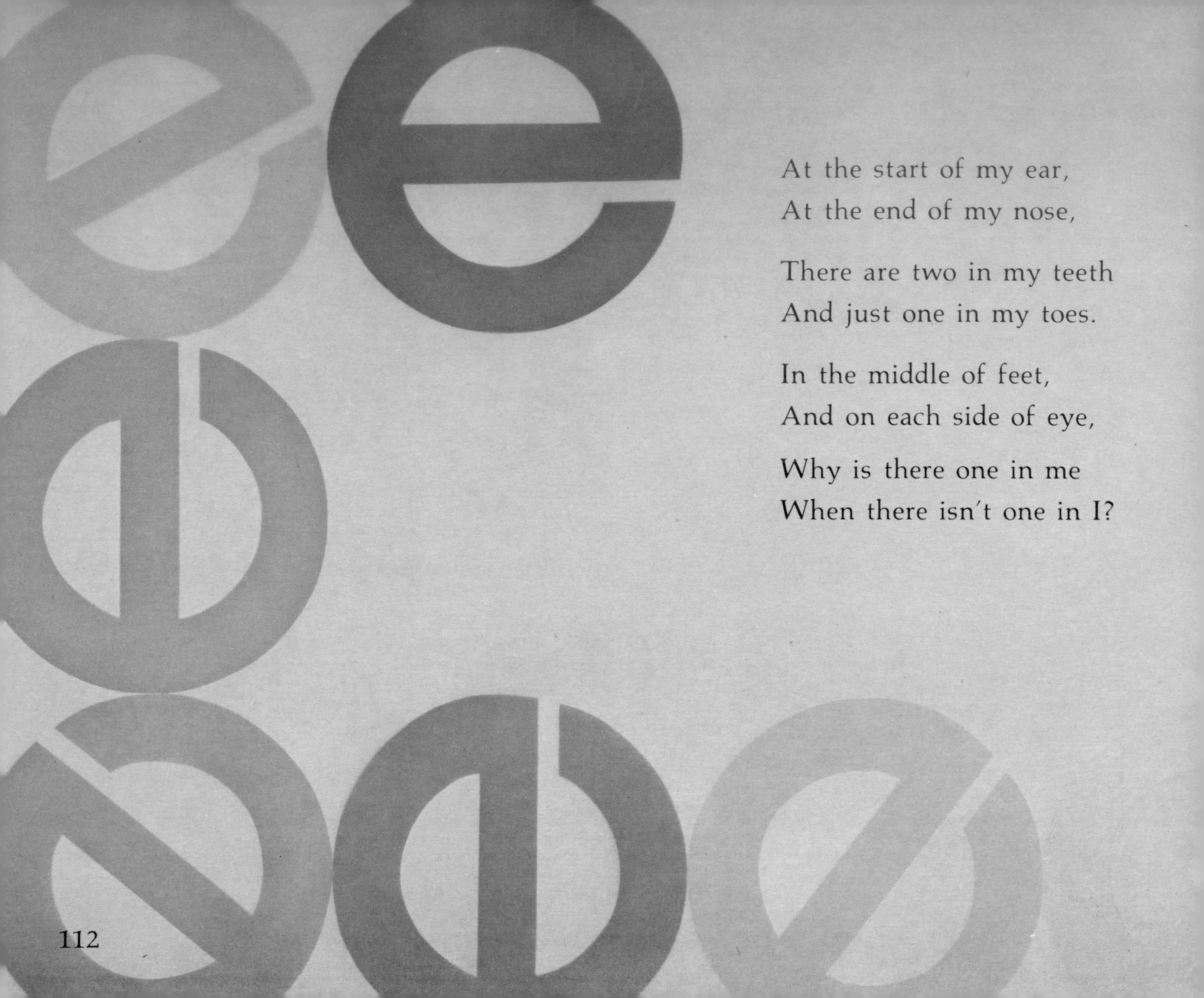

At the start of my ear,
At the end of my nose,

There are two in my teeth
And just one in my toes.

In the middle of feet,
And on each side of eye,

Why is there one in me
When there isn't one in I?

early

Quite a few things
haven't happened to me yet.
I go to bed too early.

Richard J. Margolis

eat

Marsha really likes to eat ice cream.

He'll be sorry he said that.
Just watch. He'll eat his words!

What's eating him?
He's been mad all day.

Joan really loves baseball.
She just eats it up.

eavesdrop

to listen secretly to people talking

Who is the eavesdropper?

echo

If you're in a high place like a mountain,

Or an empty space
like a tunnel,

Or a deep place
like a well,

AND YOU YELL,
Your voice
comes back to you.
And that is an echo.

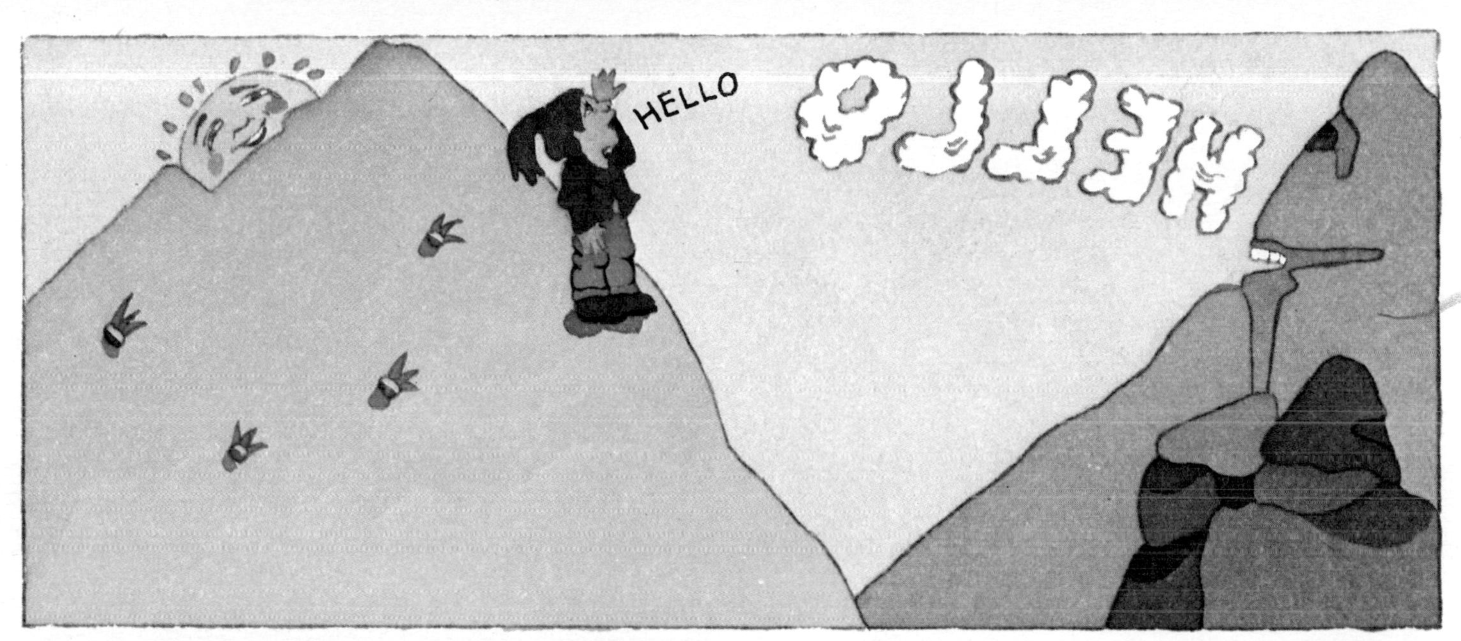
HELLO

HELLO
This is a recording.
Because of a sore throat,
the echo is not working
today.

ecology

Ecology is the study of plants and animals and air and water and the way people treat them. This story shows that if people spoil the water for plants and animals, they also spoil it for themselves.

Can Blue River be saved? Once it was clean and beautiful. Now it is dirty and ugly. Oh, Blue River, how did it happen?

Long ago, the Indians were the only people in the Blue River valley. They drank the river water. They caught many kinds of fish. Big trees and bright wildflowers grew around the Indian village.

Many living things made Blue River their home. Dragonflies and frogs laid their eggs in the water. Turtles ate the green water plants. Water birds made their nests near quiet pools. Other animals came down to the river to drink.

For many years only the animals and the Indians lived beside Blue River. But then other people came. They cut down the trees and made farms. They built stores. More people came and built houses. A town began to grow on the banks of Blue River.

The Indians went away. Many of the wild animals left, too.

The town grew larger. People wanted to keep the town clean, so they threw their garbage into the river. The flowing waters carried the garbage away. Still the town grew. People wanted it to be modern. They built sewers. The sewers carried waste from kitchens and bathrooms to the river. The flowing waters carried the sewage away.

The town became a city. Factories were built. Chemicals from the factories were dumped into the river, and the flowing waters carried the chemicals away. The river water that flowed into the city was still clean. But the river water that flowed out of the city was full of garbage, sewage, and chemicals. The river was polluted.

More and more new towns grew along the banks of the river. Garbage, sewage, and chemicals from each new town were dumped into the water. There was more and more pollution in the river.

Today the water of Blue River is no longer safe to drink. Insects and water plants cannot live in the dirty water. Frogs' eggs cannot hatch. The fish are dying because there are no plants or bugs to eat. Water birds no longer build their nests along the banks of the river because there are no fish for them to eat.

Many people are sad about the river. They would like Blue River to be clean and beautiful again.

Can Blue River be saved? Yes, Blue River can be saved if people work together. Blue River can be saved if people stop putting garbage into it. The river can be saved if the towns stop dumping sewage. It can be saved if the factories stop pouring chemicals into the river.

Once Blue River is clean, the insects and fish will come back. The birds that feed on the insects will build their nests along the bank once more.

People can pick up trash along the river. New trees and flowers can be planted on the banks to make the river beautiful again.

Blue River can be saved. Cleaning up the river will take time and money. Do people care enough? Will Blue River be saved?

Julian May

egg

Humpty Dumpty sat on a wall.
Humpty Dumpty had a great fall.
All the King's horses and all the King's men,
Came and ate scrambled eggs.

Eggs are not just something to eat. They are used to make paint, ink, soap, and shampoo.

Have an egg-and-spoon race with a buddy. You each need a spoon with an egg on it. (Make sure the egg is hard-boiled!) Then see who can run farther without dropping the egg.

If you soak a hard-boiled egg in vinegar overnight, the shell will get so soft that the egg will bounce.

Eggs-pert: someone who always makes perfect scrambled eggs.

The ostrich wins the prize for laying the largest bird's egg. An egg can be 6 inches long and weigh 2½ pounds.

egret

a beautiful white bird

I Didn't Want a Pet Egret

But why can't I have a pet?

Now don't get upset.
You had a turtle,
The one you called Mertle.
You put it in the wash,
And it came out like squash.

But I am older now,
And I know just how
To take care of my pet.
I want an egret.

Forget the egret.

How about a yak?
No flak from a yak.

We are getting off the track.

A mole! I want a mole!
A mole's my goal.

Hot dog! A wart hog!

Forget the hog.
Will you take a dog?

Cut the rigamarole.

Bingo! A flamingo!

Cut the lingo!

Well, if all I can get
Is a dog for a pet,
I guess that's all right.

Phew! What a fight!

elbow

where your arm bends

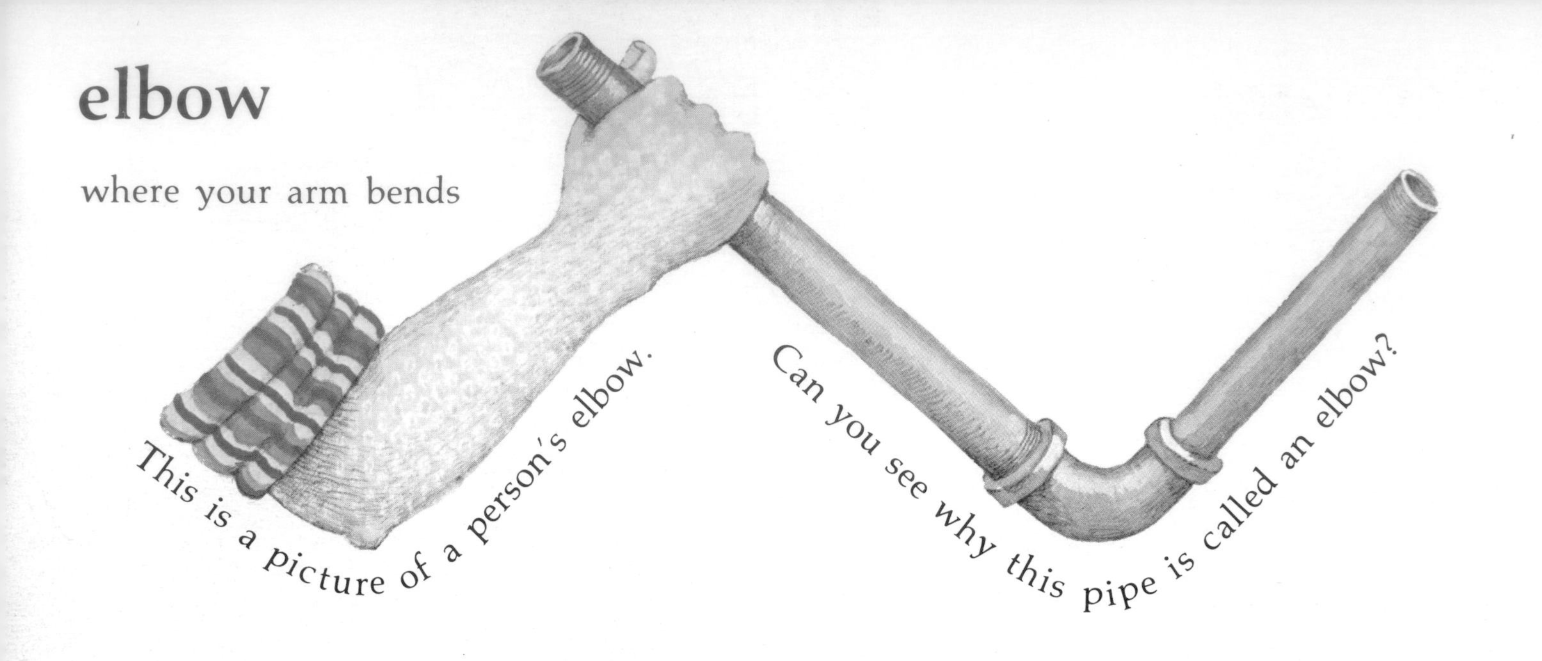

elephant

elevator

a machine that makes it easy to go up and down inside a building

Miranda lives on the twelfth floor of an apartment building. One day she got into the elevator alone on the first floor. She pushed the button for floor 8. She got off on the eighth floor and walked up the stairs to floor 12. Why didn't Miranda take the elevator to the twelfth floor?

Find the answer on page 334.

episode

a part of a story

There are four episodes in this story.

Playing Checkers at the Carpenter's

The carpenter liked things to be perfect. His overalls were always clean, and there was a pocket for everything. He could make anything.

"Bring me a picture of what you want me to make," he would say. "If I have a picture, everything will come out fine."

Across the river from the carpenter lived a tinker. He called himself a do-dadder. He could do a little bit of everything. His overalls were dirty and wrinkled. He carried a bag that was full of all sorts of things. He could do almost anything—but nothing perfectly.

"Tell me what you want," he would say. "I'll think of some way to make it."

The tinker and the carpenter had built their own houses. They were as

different as two houses could be. The carpenter's was a neat little cabin. It was all made out of wood, and everything had a place. The tinker's house was made out of old boxes, tin cans, and broken boards. It was stuck together with anything that he could find.

One Saturday morning the carpenter called across the river. "How about a game of checkers?" he shouted to the tinker.

"I'll be right over," the tinker called back.

The carpenter could not believe his eyes. The tinker jumped into the river, clothes and all, and swam across.

The carpenter brought out his checkers and checkerboard and a table with matching chairs.

"I made these checkers," he said proudly. "There are twelve black ones and twelve red ones. And they are all perfectly round."

"They are very nice," said the tinker politely.

They sat down to play. The carpenter was very careful—and very slow. He would look at the board for ages before each move. The tinker made a move as soon as it was his turn. Then he waited. He tapped his fingers. He whistled. He fidgeted. Finally the carpenter won.

"That was a great game," the carpenter said happily. "You certainly play fast."

"Yes," answered the tinker. "And you certainly play carefully. Let's play at my house next Saturday."

"O.K.," said the carpenter. "But I don't know how to swim."

"Use the bridge," said the tinker.

"You are such a quick thinker!" cried the carpenter. "But I don't know

where it is. Will you draw a map to show me the way?"

The carpenter pulled a nice sharp pencil out of his pocket. He pulled a clean piece of paper out of another pocket. Carefully, he handed them to the tinker. The tinker drew some lines here and some X's there and gave the map to the carpenter.

"Good-bye," said the tinker. "See you next Saturday." Then he jumped into the river and swam back, clothes and all.

Playing Checkers at the Tinker's

The carpenter got to the tinker's late Saturday morning. He was hot and tired.

"Let's play," said the tinker.

"Where are your checkers?" asked the carpenter.

"Oh dear," cried the tinker. "I thought you were bringing yours. I don't have any."

"I wouldn't bring my checkers," said the carpenter. "They might get lost on the way over."

The tinker could not believe it. "Never mind," he said. "Wait here. I'll find something."

He ran into his tumbledown house. When he came out his arms were full. "Here we go," he said. Then he put a checkered tablecloth over an old box.

"Here's a checkerboard," he said.

From his pockets he pulled bottle caps, jelly beans, buttons, scraps of paper, and a dusty cracker or two.

"And here are the checkers," the tinker said. "Now let's play."

They sat on boxes and played. This time the tinker won.

"That was a great game," the tinker said.

"I guess so," the carpenter said. "But I couldn't win. I never knew which checkers were mine."

"No excuses," said the tinker.

"And how could I think when you kept whistling and moving about? You sure make it hard on a careful player like me," the carpenter said unhappily.

"I almost go to sleep when I play with you," said the tinker. "I have to wait for hours for you to make a move."

The carpenter stood up and pulled the map out of his pocket. "Look at this map. I almost got lost because it was so messy. I came over here just to please you."

"Who crossed the river last week?" the tinker yelled back.

They stood there and looked at each other.

"All right," the tinker said. "Next week you use your checkers. I'll use my checkers. We'll each build a boat. Then we can meet halfway across the river."

"That's a good idea," said the carpenter. "I will see you next Saturday."

Building the Boats

The tinker had never built a boat before. Neither had the carpenter. Each set about it in his own way.

The carpenter looked at books until he found a picture of the boat he wanted. Then he copied the plans very carefully. He made sure everything was perfect. Then he began to build.

The tinker looked through his trash. He put everything that looked useful in a pile. Then he began sticking it all together.

They both worked from morning to night. They worked all week. The carpenter followed his plans very carefully. The tinker had no plans. He just put things together where they seemed to fit.

From time to time they would look across the river. They each wanted to see how the other was getting along.

"This is the best boat you ever will see!" the carpenter called out proudly. "Everything is perfect."

"My boat has a roof!" the tinker yelled back. "You'll have to sit in the hot sun. I'll be nice and cool in the shade under my roof."

That Saturday the tinker pushed his contraption into the water. Before he could get into it, the boat rolled over. It floated, all right, but bottom up, with the roof under water.

"Look at that," the carpenter laughed from the other side. "Your boat is upside down. Ha, ha."

"So what," said the tinker. "It floats." He stepped on the bottom of his boat. He held his checkers high above his head.

"Let's see *your* boat, smarty," he cried.

The carpenter pushed his boat into the water. He stepped in proudly and raised the sail. It floated along perfectly.

"You see. Just as I planned," the carpenter said, waving at the tinker.

Suddenly, ooooops!

A puff of wind hit the sail. Over went the little boat.

"Help! Help! I can't swim!" the carpenter cried.

"You can't sail, either!" the tinker said. "You left the wind out of your plans!" But he dropped his checkers and jumped into the water.

The tinker grabbed the carpenter by the overalls and pulled him out of the water.

"You weigh a ton," said the tinker.

"Yes," said the carpenter. "My tools, you know."

The tinker could not believe it. The carpenter still had his heavy tools in his pockets.

"But you were sinking! And the

heavy tools made you sink faster. Why didn't you throw your tools away?" the tinker asked.

"Well," said the carpenter, "I didn't think of it."

"You might have drowned," the tinker said.

"I guess so," said the carpenter. "But that wasn't in the plan."

"I just don't believe it," sighed the tinker.

Then he started to smile.

"Eureka!" he said. "I know! Let's build a boat together! You make the plans. We can work on it together. Then I'll take care of the emergencies."

"You always have good ideas," said the carpenter.

And so they built their boat, a beautiful one, and spent many happy days on the river together, playing checkers.

Alan Venable

eyefooler

something that tricks your eyes

man
in the
the moon

What does this say?
Did eye fool you?

Which one is longest?

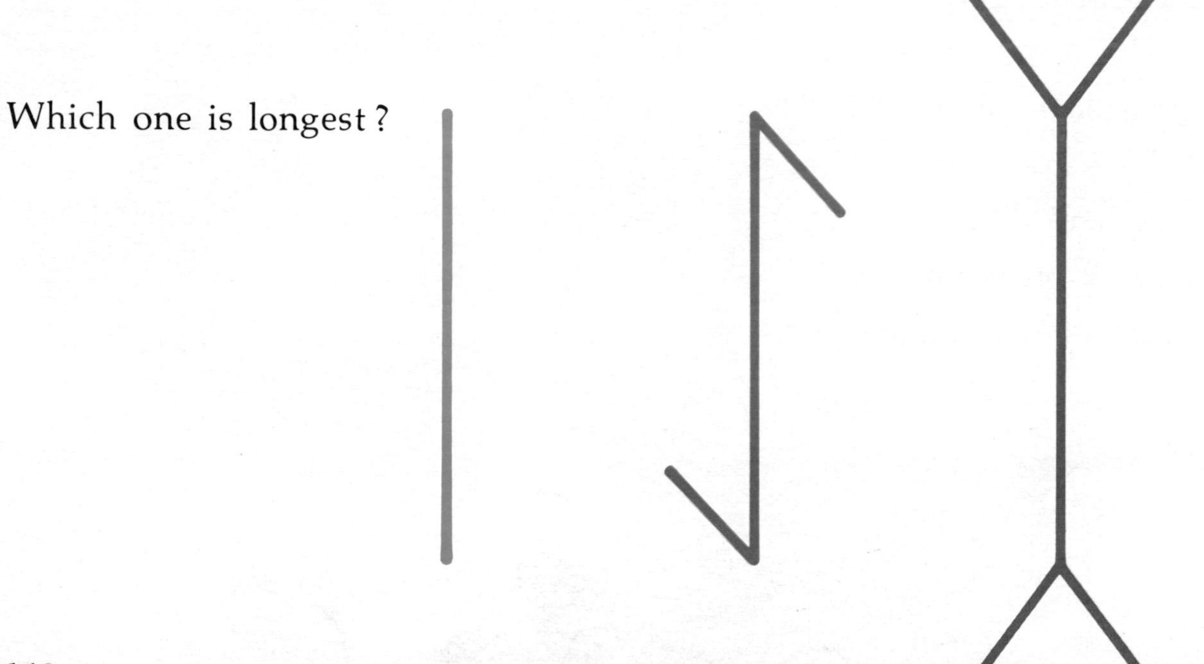

family

Standing there before the crowd
I tried to say the months out loud.
I mixed up April with November
And left out some
I couldn't remember.
All the rest I think were straight.
My family clapped and called me great.
Maybe they weren't listening.

Richard J. Margolis

famous

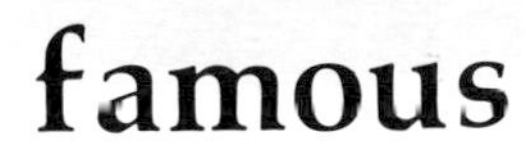

very well known

The Girl Who Painted Wallpaper

Anna Munga had started painting wallpaper when she was very little. At first she made only small paintings. Then she got bored and started painting long rolls. Her parents didn't mind at all. The long rolls kept Anna Munga quiet and busy. Soon there were stacks of wallpaper all over her room. Anna Munga's toys, which she never used, were buried.

Almost anything gave Anna Munga a new idea for wallpaper. One day she saw a bird fly by her window. She quickly painted a roll of bird wallpaper.

On another day, Anna Munga begged for more ice cream for supper. When she didn't get it, she drew it instead. In just three hours Anna Munga finished seven rolls of ice cream wallpaper. After drawing all that ice cream, she didn't want any.

By the time she was nine, Anna Munga had wallpapered her room nine different times.

She was just getting ready to wallpaper the living room for the sixth time when a stranger walked by. Who would have thought that this stranger was a famous wallpaper maker from the big city?

When the stranger saw the wallpaper in the kitchen, he just stood and stared. Anna Munga invited him to come in.

"Where did you get that beautiful wallpaper?" asked the stranger.

"I made it," answered Anna Munga. "I do it just for fun."

"For fun?" asked the stranger. "Why don't you do it for money? I am a famous wallpaper maker. You can become rich and famous, too."

Sure enough, that famous wallpaper maker was telling the truth. All Anna Munga had to do was to make one little roll. Then she put it into a machine. The machine made other rolls exactly like it much faster than she could paint them herself.

Anna Munga and the big machine made wallpaper for every house in town. On some houses, Anna Munga suggested hanging wallpaper on the outside, too. Soon everybody wanted wallpaper on the outside of the house.

Anna Munga became famous. She was very rich. Reporters wanted reports. Moviemakers wanted movies. And besides wanting to see and hear the little girl, people were screaming for more wallpaper. So the wallpaper maker built a new machine. This one needed just the first little bit of Anna Munga's painting in order to make millions of rolls.

Then one day Anna Munga realized that she was not happy anymore. She was rich. She was famous. But she hadn't painted even one roll of new wallpaper in six months because no one ever left her alone to work.

Anna Munga knew she had to get away. She knew that she was only happy when she was painting wallpaper. So she thought of places to hide. She thought and thought until late at night. Then she got an idea.

She locked herself into her giant workroom. She was extra careful and put nine locks on the door. Then Anna Munga started spreading blank rolls of paper all over the floor. She put paper on the walls and all over the ceiling. By the time morning came, she could hear everyone outside the room. The reporters, the moviemakers, and the wallpaper makers were all talking together. Anna Munga worked as fast as she could.

By dinnertime the crowd was upset and noisy.

"Let us in!" they cried. "What are you making?"

"We're breaking down the door!" they yelled.

And they broke in. But they were in for a surprise.

Famous, rich, and clever Anna Munga had painted hundreds of rolls of wallpaper to look like hundreds of Anna Mungas painting wallpaper.

The famous wallpaper maker couldn't find the real Anna Munga. The moviemakers and reporters couldn't either. Not even her parents could find her. Anna Munga was lost!

And so she lived and painted

happily ever after
happily ever after
happily ever after
happily ever after
happily ever after
happily ever after
happily ever after
happily ever after

Mark Rubin

A feather is a letter from a bird.

Beatrice Schenk de Regniers

The words *fir* and *fur* sound alike but have different meanings.

fir: a kind of tree   fur: animal hair

Fuzzy Wuzzy was a bear,
Fuzzy Wuzzy had no hair,
Fuzzy Wuzzy wasn't fuzzy, was he?

Was Fuzzy Wuzzy firry or furry?

Neither one. He wasn't firry or furry. He had no hair at all.

The Fire That Saved

There was nothing Hamaguchi liked to do better than watch the village wake up. From his house high on the hill, he could see the town below. He stood and watched the fresh morning light creep over the village.

He watched fishermen go off in small wooden boats.

He watched women whip wet clothes on the stones in the stream.

He watched farmers climb the hill to their rice fields above the village.

And then Hamaguchi turned to his own fields and watched the sun dance over them. His eyes rested on the rice stalks. They had been cut and tied together. In the morning light, each bundle looked like a mountain of captured sunbeams.

"There is something good about spending your old age growing things," thought Hamaguchi.

The old man cared for each bundle of rice as he would have cared for a grandchild. He worried about the rice as it grew. He was proud when the rice was harvested. The rice fields made Hamaguchi happier than anything else.

The morning passed quickly. Hamaguchi worked in his fields and then took a nap. In the afternoon, he helped some children mend a broken kite. In the evening, he cooked dinner. All was peaceful.

Suddenly the house rocked. It was an earthquake. Usually Hamaguchi would not have worried. There were often little earthquakes. But this was different. Hamaguchi waited and watched the sea.

There it was! The water was turning from blue to deep plum-purple. Far away, Hamaguchi saw a giant wave beginning to grow.

There was little time. The people in the village could not see the wave. Somehow, Hamaguchi must warn them. But how? He was too old to run there in time.

Hamaguchi hurried inside. He grabbed a stick and lit it in the stove. Then he went to his fields. One by one, he touched each bundle of rice with the burning stick. One by one, the bundles burst into flame. Soon black smoke stained the sky.

And still the wave grew.

It was not long before everyone in the village was crying, "Hamaguchi's fields are burning! Come! We must help him!"

And still the giant wave grew higher.

The people filled pans and buckets with water. They hurried up the hill to put out the fire.

But when they got there, they were surprised. The old man was just sitting quietly.

"Hamaguchi! Why do you sit while your fields burn?" they asked.

Hamaguchi said nothing. He just pointed to the sea.

The sea! The sea was rising! It was rising like a giant tower!

"Tsunami!" they all cried. "Tidal wave!" Then they, too, were silent. The dark wave came on.

Everyone stood as still as stone. Everyone stood and watched.

Suddenly the giant wave rushed toward the village. As it struck, the wave tore at the land. One, two, three times it hit. Fields, homes, and boats

were ripped away. Then, after one last roar, the sea was quiet.

The people stared down at what had once been their village. Now there was nothing left. There was nothing left at all.

At last Hamaguchi spoke. "That is why I set fire to my fields. I knew that when you saw my fields burning, you would hurry up the mountain to help."

He looked at the village below and said, "Your homes are gone, but you are safe. My house remains. Come, there is room for many."

And Hamaguchi turned and led the way.

Lafcadio Hearn

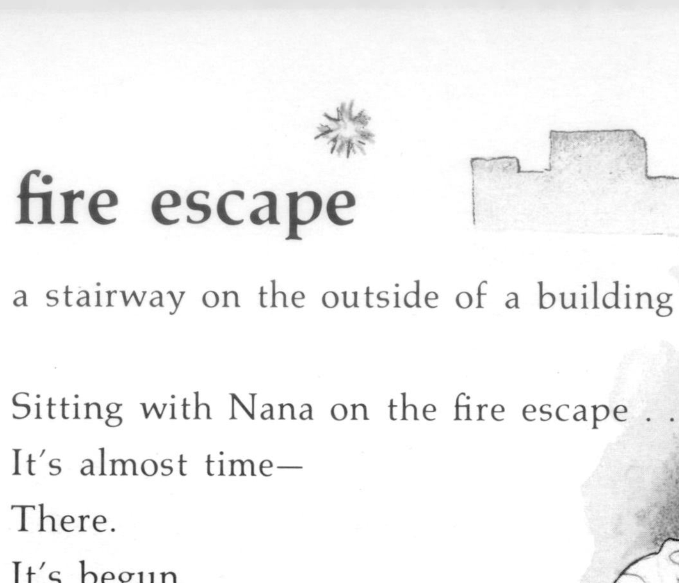

fire escape

a stairway on the outside of a building

Sitting with Nana on the fire escape . . .
It's almost time—
There.
It's begun.
At last.
The best part of the day,
When the sky is tangerine
And the buildings
Ripe cherries.

Listen . . .
The birds calling. Twippering.

And the sun . . .
Setting so slowly,
Sinking,

Sprinkling
A shower of golden sparkles
Everywhere.

"Look," says Nana. "It's a sun shower."

And we laugh and laugh.

Gone . . .
All of a sudden, the sun's just gone.

Quiet . . .
Night sky.
All green
And blue
And still.

fish

There once was a man named Thatchery
Who raised salmon in his fish hatchery.
When the salmon were grown,
They were left on their own,
To swim up the river quite naturally.

A woman whose name was Ms. Tish
Once wanted to catch a large fish.
She threw in her line,
Said, "A salmon is mine!
There's nothing like getting your wish!"

Ms. Cuzzen sells fish in her store
And tells all who come to her door:
"Fresh salmon's a treat,
Delicious to eat,
I know that you'll come back for more."

When Old Fred cooks Salmon Delight,
His friends get a huge appetite.
They get on their knees,
Saying, "Please, oh yes, please,
Dear Fred, let us have just one bite."

When salmon is served to young Nate,
He says, "Boy oh boy is this great.
All fish is just fine,
But salmon's divine—
I love it; please fill up my plate!"

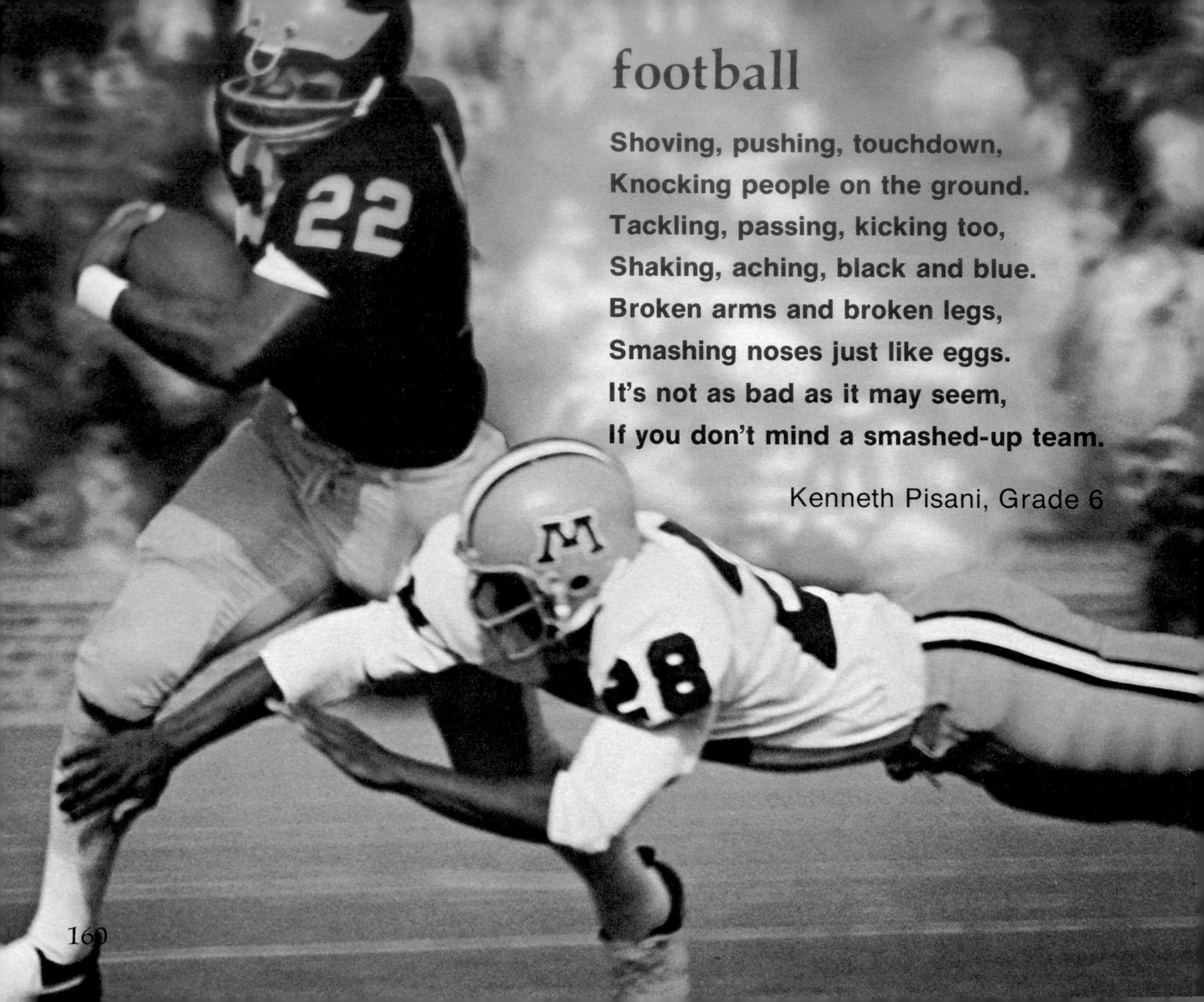

football

Shoving, pushing, touchdown,
Knocking people on the ground.
Tackling, passing, kicking too,
Shaking, aching, black and blue.
Broken arms and broken legs,
Smashing noses just like eggs.
It's not as bad as it may seem,
If you don't mind a smashed-up team.

Kenneth Pisani, Grade 6

fortress

Long, long ago a fortress was a safe place to go in times of war.

Imagine that

. . . You went to this fortress to escape danger.
How does the moat help to keep you safe?
Why does the fortress have small windows?
Why does it have a drawbridge?
Why are the walls thick?
Why does the fortress have turrets?

frontier

the wild part of a country where people have not yet built towns

Raising cattle on the frontier was hard work. The cattle had to be moved long distances to find food and water. The land they traveled through was rough and dangerous.

Many people had to help with the cattle. Cowpunchers moved the cattle from place to place. They made sure the animals stayed together. Even after dark, night herders made sure the cattle didn't wander off.

The cook went with the cowpunchers from camp to camp. The cook's wagon was called a chuck wagon. It was like a moving kitchen. Food was locked in the wagon's chuck box, and only the cook had the key.

The cook had to make meals without a stove. He cooked over a campfire. But some food, like beans, had to be baked for a long time. The cook would dig a hole and put rocks in it. Then he lit a fire on the rocks. When the fire went out and the rocks were hot, he buried pots of food in the hole. Cowpunchers could always find warm food in the bean-hole.

Elinore Stewart moved from a city to the Wyoming frontier. The letters she wrote to her friends told stories about frontier life.

September 13, 1912

Dear Joanna,

I rode over to visit Suzanne last week. It turned out to be quite a trip. She has five hundred cattle that she wanted to check on. So we put a few things in the wagon, and off we went.

When we got to camp, no one was there. The fire was out. The back of the chuck wagon was closed up and locked. Suzanne called, but no one answered. So we made the best of it. We tied the horses and went down to the river to clean up. Suzanne was mad that the cook wasn't in camp. She said that she would fire him.

Just then we saw the funniest thing. It was the

fat cook, Herman. He was riding on a thin, tired, old horse that could barely carry him.

Before Herman could say a word, Suzanne started to yell.

"How can it be?" she shouted. "We come to camp so hungry, and what do we find? Nothing. No cook and no food."

Herman answered just as loudly, "How can it be you say? And you have lived this long in the West and still don't know enough to hunt a bean-hole?"

Luckily, they both started to laugh. Then Herman took the stones from where the fire had been. He lifted out some pots from the hole. They were full of meat, beans, and potatoes. Did that food smell good!

Herman got some bread and pie from the chuck box. He put a cloth on the ground for us to eat from. He was surprised at how much food we ate. I ate a good many ashes with my meat. We both ate

some sand. But out here you don't worry about that.

Soon the cowpunchers rode in. They came right over to the fire and the food. They ate hungrily from their tin plates.

It started to get cold. The sky grew dark. Soon the cowpunchers were busy again. Fresh ponies were being saddled for the night herders. The tired horses were turned loose. They would graze all night.

Suzanne and I settled down. I have never been more tired. But I couldn't fall asleep. I could hear someone giving orders. The cowpunchers were talking about their day. Herman was clanging pots and pans as he put them away.

Then Herman called, "Cackle-berries for breakfast tomorrow. Get up early. First come, first served."

"Cackle-berries?" I wondered.

I woke up to the same noise—Herman clanging on a tin pan. "Cackle-berries," he shouted. "Cackle-berries and steak for breakfast."

I dressed as fast as I could. I could not wait to try those berries. Wild berries for breakfast would be a treat. I was one of the first ones ready. The punchers were surprised to see me at the fire so soon. I held out my tin plate. Herman gave me some steak, two eggs, and biscuits. We had coffee in big cups. When I finished my food, I told Herman that I was ready for cackle-berries.

"Listen to her now, will you?" he said. "How many more cackle-berries do you want?"

"Why Herman, I haven't had any," I said.

What a roar of laughter! Then Herman explained that eggs and cackle-berries were the same thing. I began to laugh as hard as the rest. In fact I laughed all the way home.

It was a great trip. And as you can tell, I am very happy with my life out west.

Very truly your friend,
Elinore Stewart

games

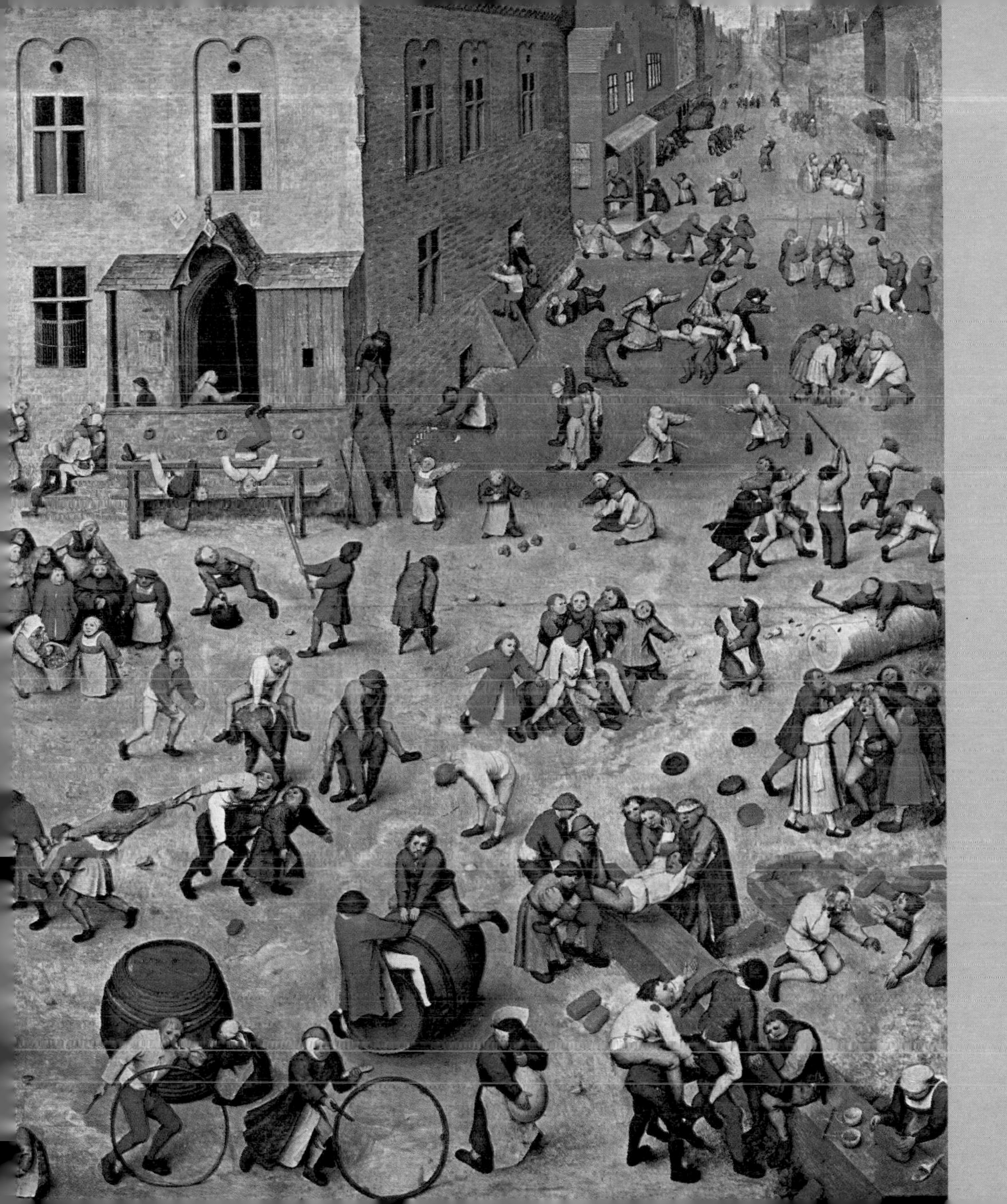

Hoopla

hOOp

hOOp

hOOp

OOps

hOOp

hOOp

whOOps

hOOp

hOOp

hOOpety

hOOpety

lOOpety

lOOps

Jacks

Jacks look like stars,
and the ball you throw to catch them
like a small red moon.
While the moon's bouncing back
your hand must be quick
to collect star after star.
The rules say
If you touch too much
or let the moon roll away
you lose the game.

Kathleen Fraser

Stilts

Stand tall
Walk tall
See all.
Stilts.

Long fall
Hard fall
Smash all.
Stilts.

Stay small
Walk small
That's all.
No stilts.

Headstand

Bend knees,
Lean on face,
Throw your feet to outer space.
Wiggle woggle twist around
to keep your head
flat on the ground.
Spread arms wide
like elephant ears,
Laugh away your falling fears.
For now,
because a hand's a foot
and foot is now a head,
a face is at the bottom, and it's turning cherry red.

gather

to harvest or pick

Potato Vacation

I am Peggy. He is my brother. We call him Rusty. He is six and three-quarters. I'm older.

We both go to the same school. It's in town, and we have to take a bus to get there. Papa has an old car, but he only takes it to town once a week to do the shopping.

We live in a farmhouse, far out in the country. There is no farm to it now, just a little bit of land, a barn, and a house.

There are lots of big farms and small farms where we live. Potato farms. Around here, all that people

think about is potatoes. I guess there are some other things they think about, but if you ask me, mostly they think about potatoes. Especially in

October. Potatoes are how just about everybody makes a living.

There is even a potato vacation. That means the schools are closed for a week when the potatoes are being harvested. My brother and I gather potatoes then. Of course, the other children and the teachers get the week off, too. They don't all go to the potato fields, but most of them do. Nobody is going to get rich picking potatoes, but you do get paid. Even kids get paid.

We have to get up very early when we gather potatoes. It is always still dark when we get up, and cold. We go down to the kitchen where it's warm by the stove. We dress there and have breakfast. Then Momma gives us lunch. We each get a box with sandwiches in it, and cookies and an apple, and some hot chocolate in a thermos. We eat in the middle of the morning because we start working so early.

Then we go out in front of the house and stand by the road. We wait in the dark for the potato bus. It's shivering cold. The bus takes us to the field where we gather the potatoes.

First the machine goes by and throws the potatoes up out of the ground. Then we gather them and put them into baskets.

In the summer the potato fields are pretty. The plants have flowers, some white, some pink, waving in their green leaves. They cover the fields like the pink and white and green patchwork quilt Grandma made.

But by potato vacation all the flowers are gone, and so are the plants. All you can see are fields of brown ground and potatoes tossed up by the machine.

At first when we get to the field, it's a little bit nice. The early morning sky is as red as apples, and there is a twinkle of frost on everything. The air is bright and still cold. I like it then.

What I do not like is gathering potatoes.

I get tired. I know what Grandma means when she says she aches all over. I ache all over by about the fourth potato. Rusty doesn't get as tired as I do, but that's because he is a slow mover. I have already put twelve potatoes in our basket by the time he's dropped one in.

He's really too young for potato vacation work. Momma didn't want him to go. But Rusty is stubborn and would not stay behind. Lots of times he wipes a potato off on his shirt and eats it. Just like that. Not washed or cooked or peeled or anything. He says it's good, but that is not so. I never eat potatoes.

Potatoes in the field look a lot like stones. It's hard sometimes to tell a stone from a potato before you pick it up. Of course, you have to throw the stone back onto the ground, not into your basket.

Mostly they let the school children go home in the afternoon. If they didn't, there would be a whole field of kids crying. Picking potatoes is such hard work. I usually feel like crying about the middle of the first basket, but I don't.

One day I was putting potatoes in our basket. My hands hurt and my back hurt and my fingernails were all broken. I thought it would be just lovely to cry. Then this big frog came along. There was a little frog, too.

"My," I said to the big frog, "what a fine-looking child you have!"

"You are nuts," said my brother.

"You'd better go," I said to the frog. "Someone might put you into a basket and sell you for a potato."

"You're crazy, Peggy!" yelled my brother. "Crazy, crazy!"

But Rusty isn't even seven, and he doesn't know that sometimes you have to talk crazy to keep from feeling crazy.

I have not decided what to be when I grow up, but I know one thing. I am not going to be a potato farmer. I really truly do not like potatoes. I don't like to pick them. I never eat them.

This was Rusty's first time picking, and he says that he wants to be a potato farmer when he grows up. But he's only six and three-quarters and doesn't know everything about himself yet.

Mary Stolz

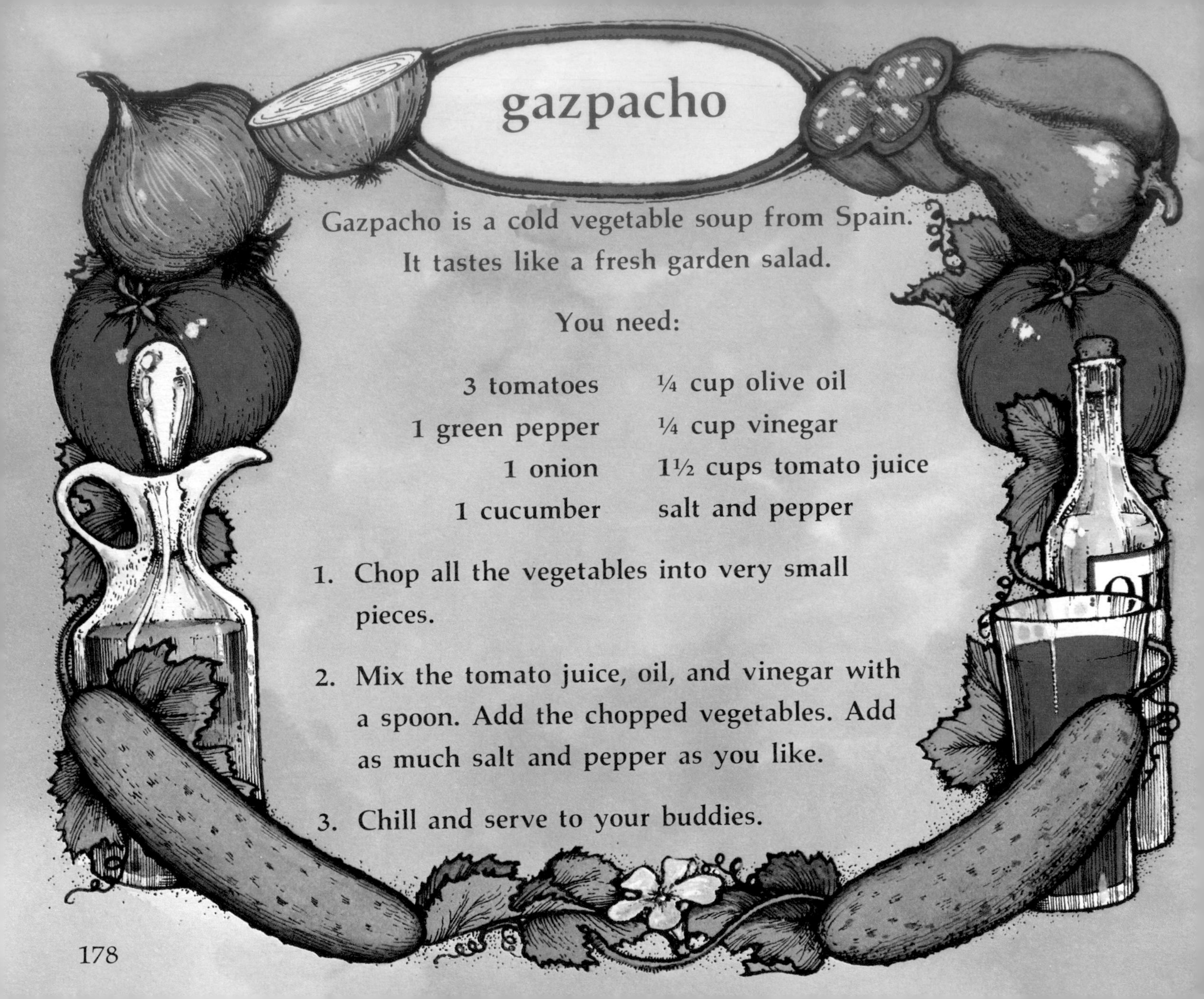

gazpacho

Gazpacho is a cold vegetable soup from Spain.
It tastes like a fresh garden salad.

You need:

3 tomatoes	¼ cup olive oil
1 green pepper	¼ cup vinegar
1 onion	1½ cups tomato juice
1 cucumber	salt and pepper

1. Chop all the vegetables into very small pieces.
2. Mix the tomato juice, oil, and vinegar with a spoon. Add the chopped vegetables. Add as much salt and pepper as you like.
3. Chill and serve to your buddies.

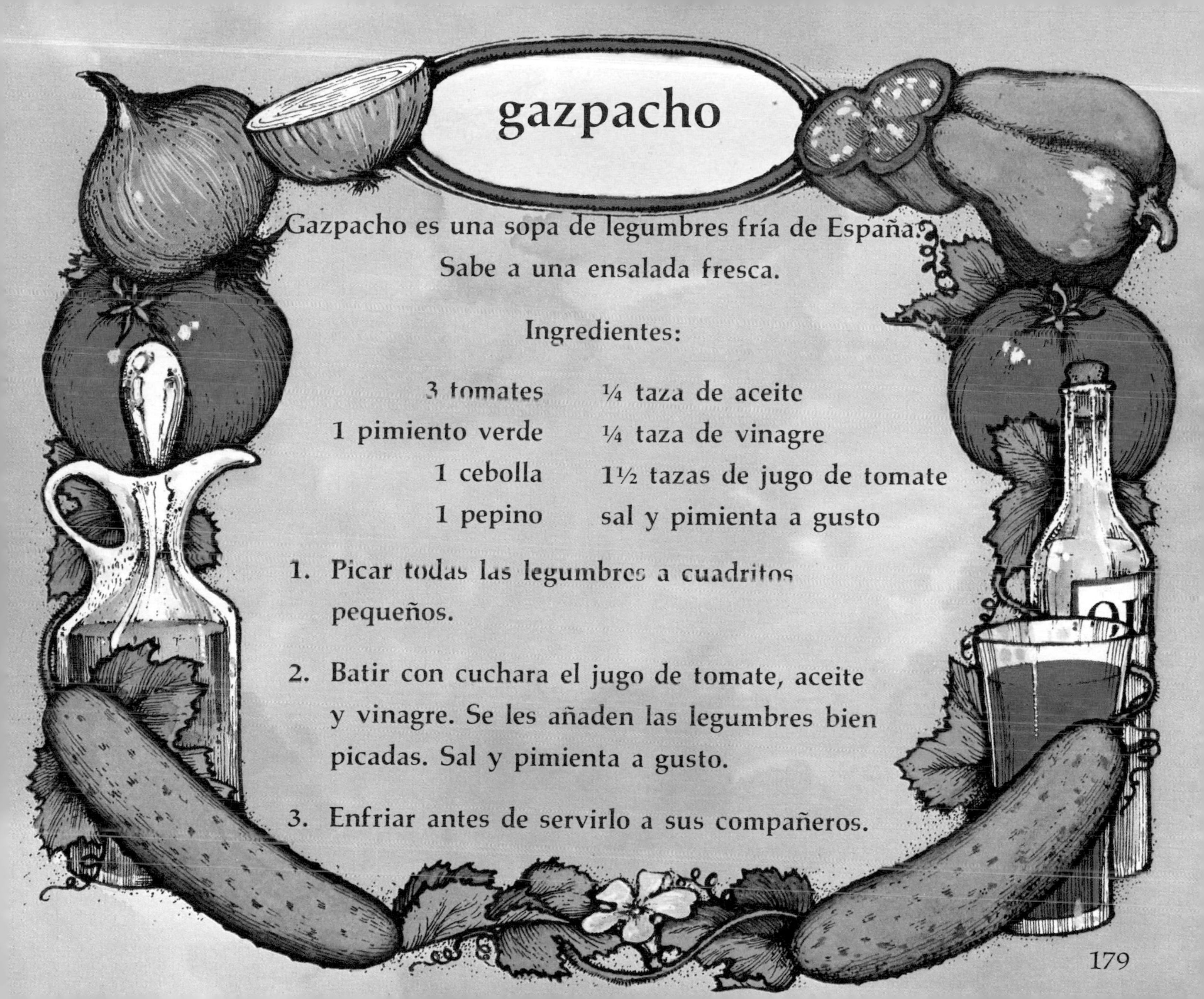

gazpacho

Gazpacho es una sopa de legumbres fría de España. Sabe a una ensalada fresca.

Ingredientes:

3 tomates	¼ taza de aceite
1 pimiento verde	¼ taza de vinagre
1 cebolla	1½ tazas de jugo de tomate
1 pepino	sal y pimienta a gusto

1. Picar todas las legumbres a cuadritos pequeños.
2. Batir con cuchara el jugo de tomate, aceite y vinagre. Se les añaden las legumbres bien picadas. Sal y pimienta a gusto.
3. Enfriar antes de servirlo a sus compañeros.

gear

a wheel with teeth

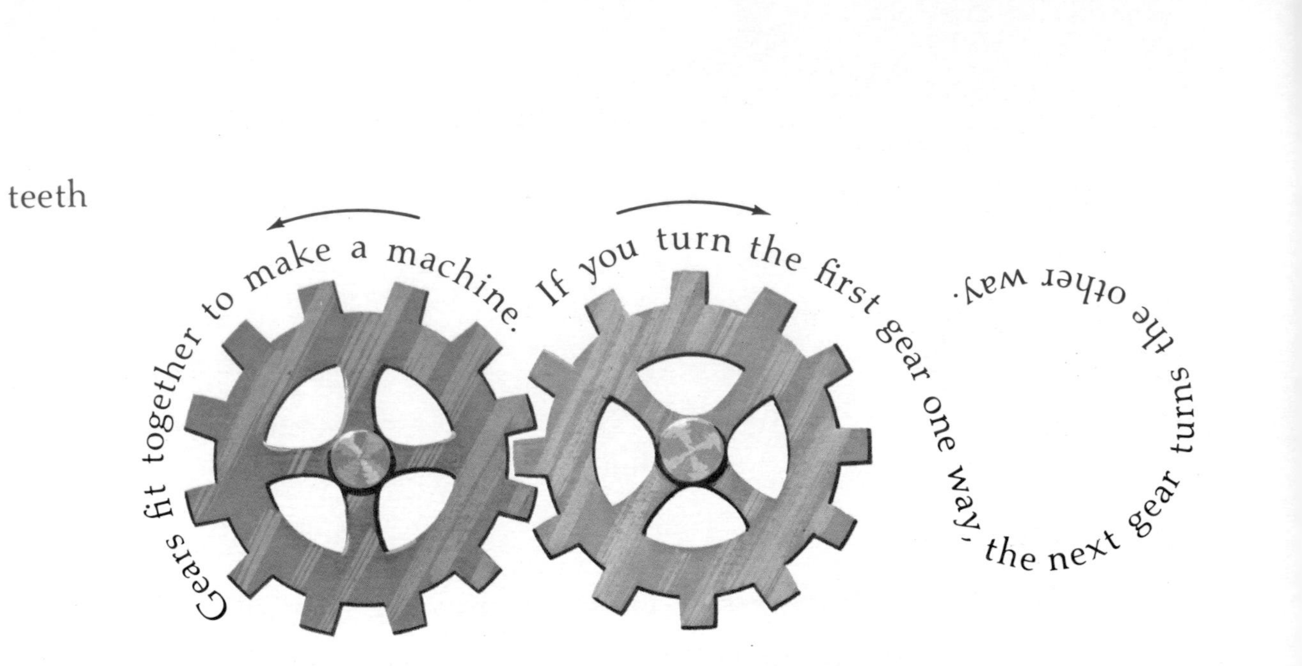

Gears fit together to make a machine. If you turn the first gear one way, the next gear turns the other way.

Which way will the last gear turn?

Find the answer on page 334.

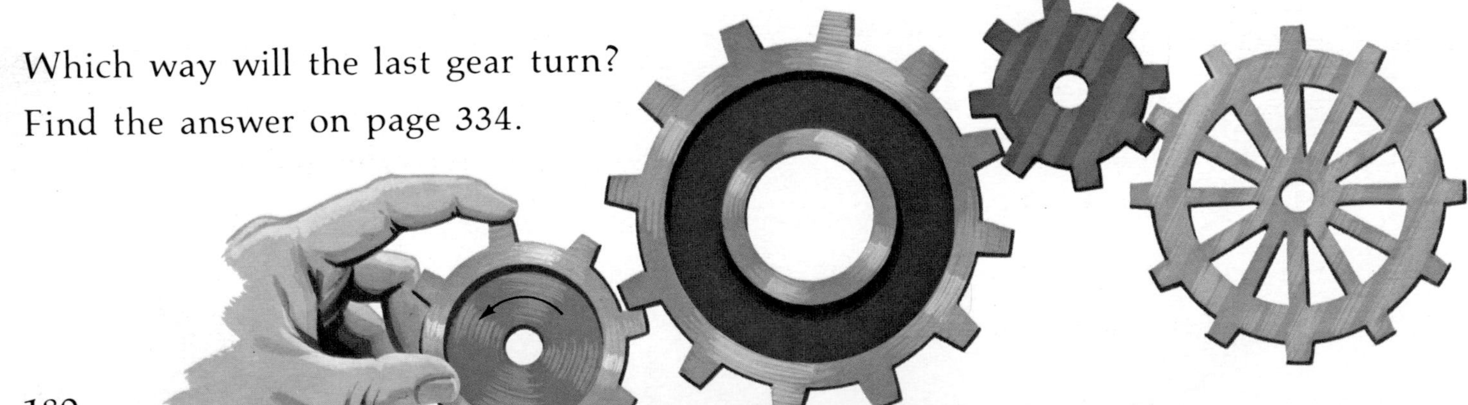

The Case of the Gingerbread Ghost

Wheezer, my dog, was lost. I had asked everyone, but no one had seen her. I had just given up asking when I heard a small voice say, "Sarah, I saw Wheezer."

It was Howie, a first-grader who lives on my street.

"Howie!" I said. "Where?"

He answered softly, "Last night I saw her. She was running toward the old Gingerbread House."

"Oh, please, no," I thought, "not the Gingerbread House."

"Then what?" I asked aloud.

"Well," he continued, "she sniffed around the door and then. . . ."

Howie stopped. He stared down at his shoes.

"Then what?" I asked again.

"She DISAPPEARED!" he shouted.

"Howie-e-e-e," I said. "Are you fibbing?"

"No, Sarah!" he said. "Cross my heart. I even called her, but she didn't come. Sarah, do you think the ghost got her?"

"No," I answered. "There are no ghosts. Come on, Howie, show me where you saw Wheezer disappear. O.K.?"

"Oh, no!" he said.

"Oh, yes!" I commanded.

I knew Howie was afraid, so I held his hand and tried to act brave. But as we came near the house, I felt cold and goosebumpy all over.

Everyone called it the Gingerbread House because the outside was decorated with carved woodwork. It looked like a fancy cake. But many of the carved decorations had been eaten away by wind and rain. Around the front and back steps, weeds grew tall and wild. The trees next to the house made scratchy noises against the sky.

Mrs. Tripstone, who lived there, owned the candy shop. Once a year, on Halloween night, she gave all the kids candy from the shop. Her house was the biggest and scariest house in the neighborhood, but her treats were the best treats in town.

Then just two weeks before Halloween, Mrs. Tripstone died. Mr. Jessy, a carpenter, came by to fix things up. The house made him nervous.

"Strange things going on in that house," Mr. Jessy said. "I can hear scratching and rattling in Mrs. Tripstone's room. But when I look—nothing is there! The place is haunted."

Soon everybody in town was talking about the Gingerbread Ghost.

It was about this same time that Wheezer started running away. She would break her chain and be gone all day, but she always came home. Except this time.

I looked at the old house. "Could Wheezer really be trapped in this spooky place?" I wondered.

Howie and I tiptoed to the front door. The steps creaked.

"Hey! You kids!"

Howie jumped.

"It's all right, Howie," I said. "It's just Mr. Jessy, the carpenter."

"What are you kids doing here?" asked Mr. Jessy.

I explained about Wheezer and asked if Howie and I could look inside the house.

Mr. Jessy leaned on his ladder and said, "Are you sure you want to go into that house?"

I nodded yes. Howie shook his head no. Mr. Jessy walked to the front door.

"There is a little pet door here," he said. "It's big enough for Wheezer to get through. But I can't let you go in."

"Please, Mr. Jessy," I said.

"Well," he said at last, "I had better go with you."

He took out his keys, and soon we were all standing inside the house.

"Wheezer," I whispered. "Are you here?"

No answer. Just a creepy-queer noise from the next room.

Scratch. Scritchy scratch.

Howie froze in his tracks.

"It's that tree out front," said Mr. Jessy. "The branches scrape against the windows."

Howie relaxed, and I was just about to tell him he could go home when Mr. Jessy spoke up and said, "Well, I think I will cut some of the branches right now, while I'm thinking of it. You kids hurry up. If you want me, just yell."

He left, and I think he expected us to leave, too. But I just stood there, holding on to Howie. I wasn't going to let him go home now. Howie was scared skinny, but I didn't want to stay in the house alone.

Quietly, we searched the first floor. We found nothing—just rooms and rooms of old furniture covered with sheets.

Howie looked at the sheets as if they were ghosts ready to jump.

"They're just sheets," I said. "Look underneath them. Wheezer may be trapped—or something."

Then, very softly, came a funny noise. We listened again.

Snuffle, snuffle. Scratch.

"Oh, Sarah," said Howie. "Let's go-o-o!"

"It's O.K., Howie," I said. "It's just Mr. Jessy working outside."

But it wasn't Mr. Jessy. The noise came from upstairs. And it was a noise that I thought I knew. I took Howie by the hand, and we went upstairs. We found nothing.

Then, once again, we heard the noise. *Snuffle, snuffle. Rattle. Scratch.*

Howie made a nose dive into the nearest chair.

"Wheezer!" I shouted. "Where are you?"

And Wheezer answered, "Wuf!"

"She's in there!" I said. I dragged Howie out of the chair, and we entered a large, dark room. It was empty!

"Wuf!" barked Wheezer again.

Then Howie did the bravest thing of his life. He opened a closet door.

"Wow!" he yelled. "Look at this!"

The closet was filled with candy. In back of the closet was a small stairway that led downstairs. Halfway down sat Wheezer. Her chain was caught on a nail. Candy boxes were scattered all down the steps.

"Wow!" said Howie again.

"Wuf!" said Wheezer.

The stairway took us back down to the kitchen.

We just reached the bottom when Mr. Jessy came back in.

"What have you been up to?" he asked.

I told him about the closet and the staircase and the candy.

Mr. Jessy looked at Wheezer and

chuckled. "Some ghost," he said.

"Wuf!" said Wheezer.

Mr. Jessy and I laughed. But Howie kept looking back up the stairs.

"Come on, Sarah!" he pleaded. "Let's go-o-o-o."

We left.

A few days later Mr. Jessy told the kids in the neighborhood to come to the Gingerbread House and get their Halloween treats.

"Mrs. Tripstone ordered that stuff for the kids," he said. "She would want them to have it."

I didn't go back. I figured Wheezer had eaten my share. And Howie? Well, Howie never figured out the connection between Wheezer and the Gingerbread Ghost. So Howie never went back, either. Howie still believes in ghosts.

giant big, large, huge,

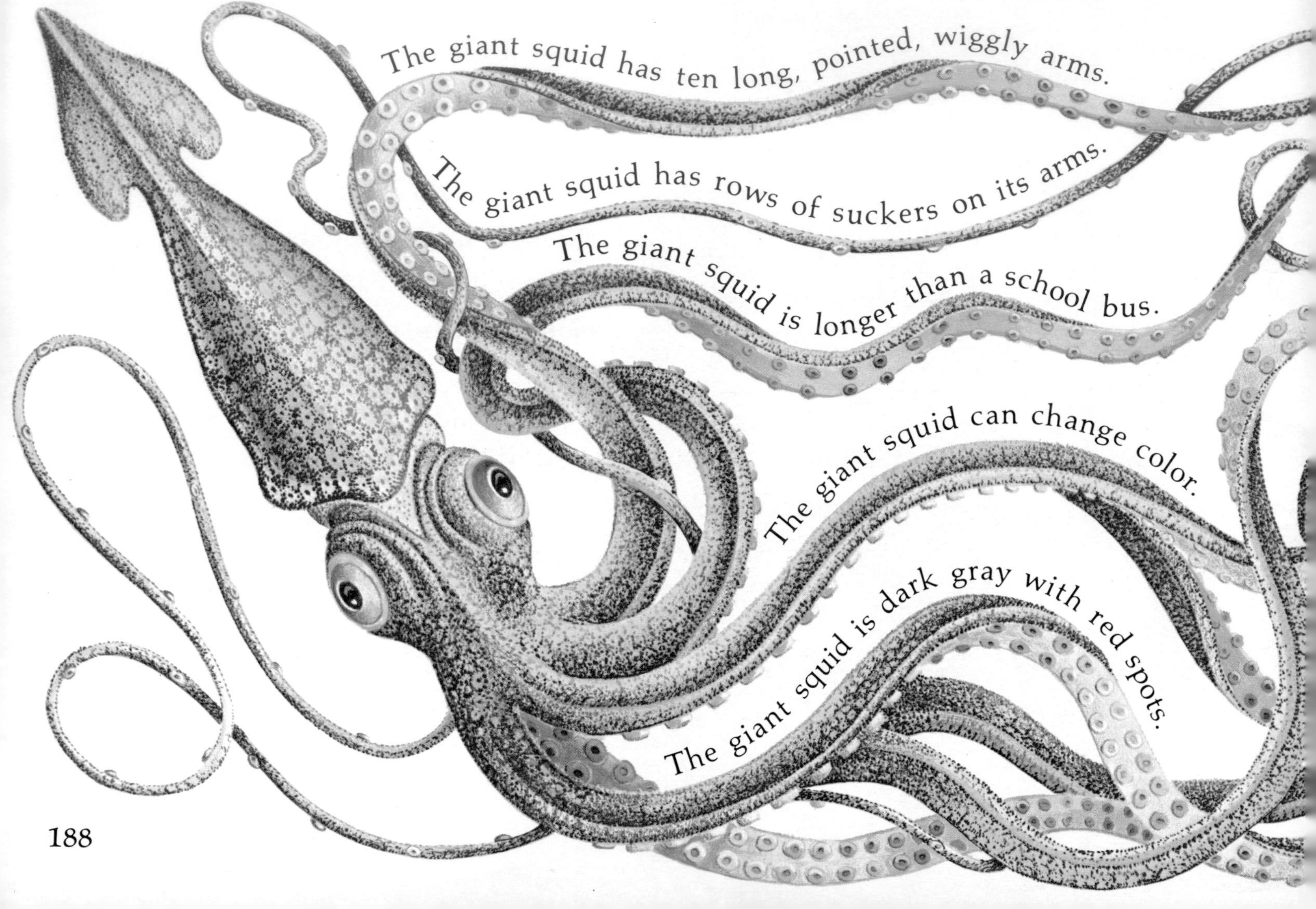

The giant squid has ten long, pointed, wiggly arms.

The giant squid has rows of suckers on its arms.

The giant squid is longer than a school bus.

The giant squid can change color.

The giant squid is dark gray with red spots.

enormous, gigantic

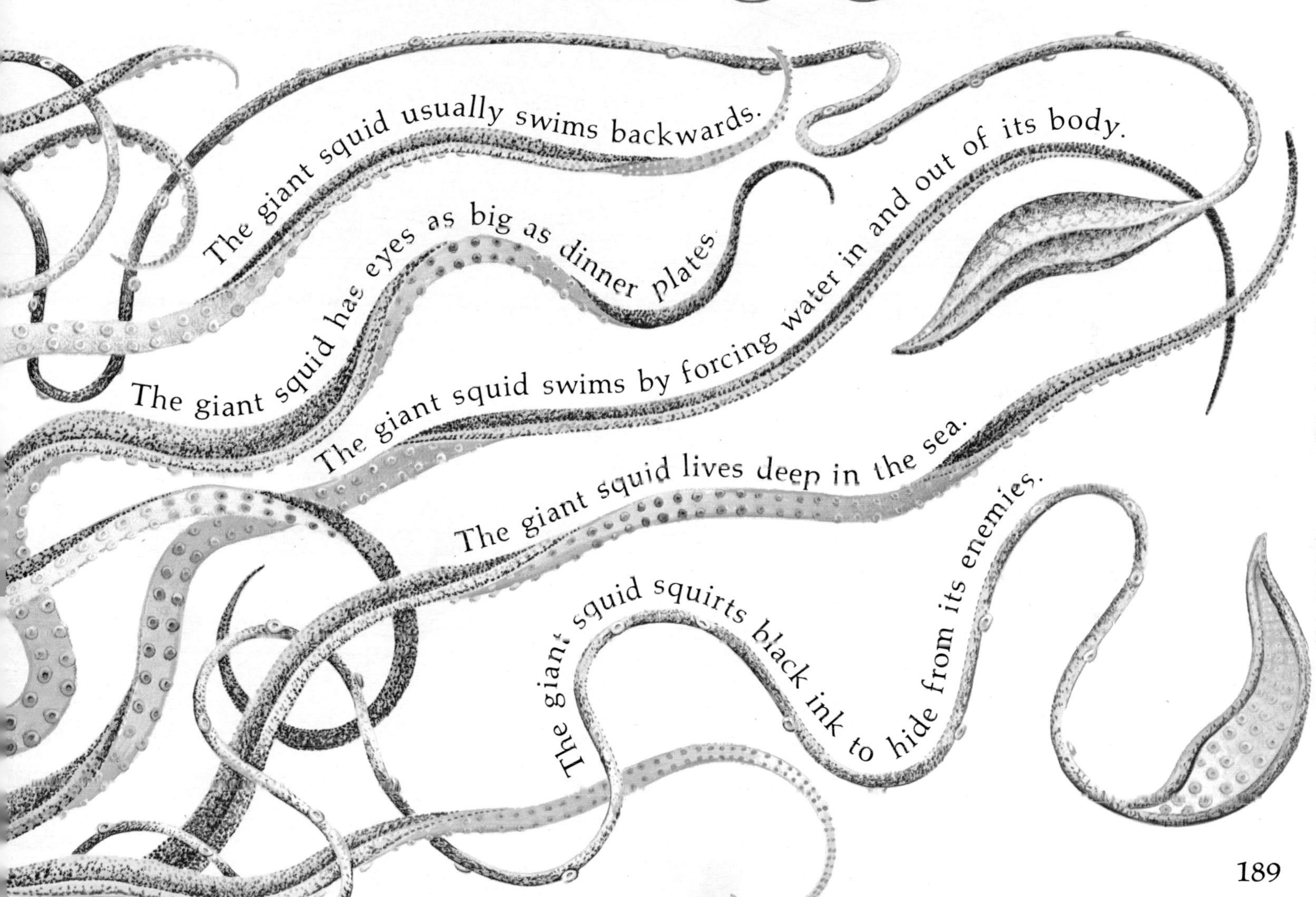

The giant squid usually swims backwards.
The giant squid has eyes as big as dinner plates.
The giant squid swims by forcing water in and out of its body.
The giant squid lives deep in the sea.
The giant squid squirts black ink to hide from its enemies.

ginger ale

a drink that feels like your foot does when it goes to sleep

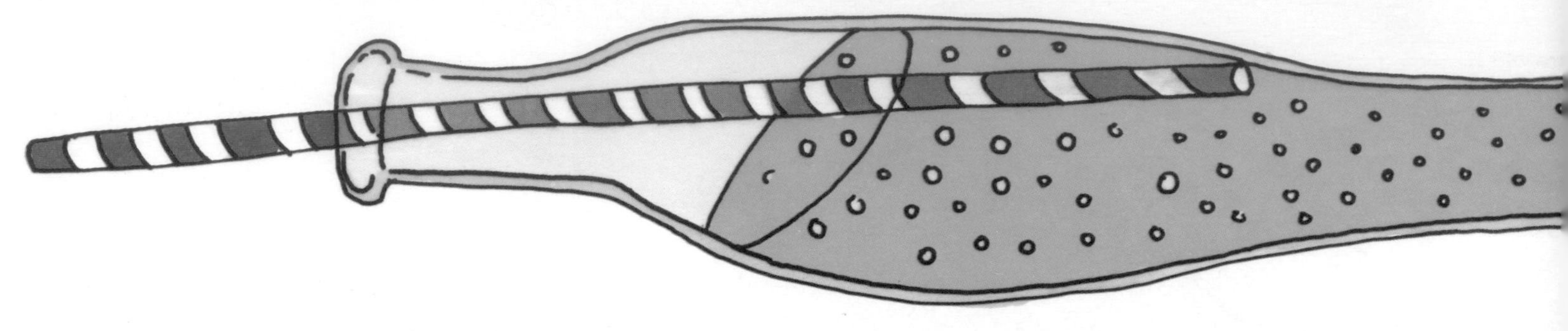

glass

Here is a trick to try on your buddy.

Take six glasses. Fill three of them with water. Ask your buddy to touch or move only one glass to make the glasses look like this:

Can you figure out this trick? Turn to page 334.

glowworm

a firefly

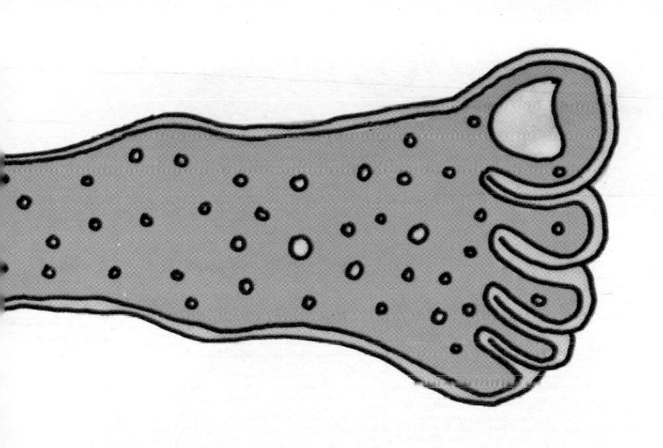

Never talk down to a glowworm—
Such as *What do you knowworm?*
How's it down belowworm?
Guess you're quite a slowworm.
No. Just say

Helloworm!

David McCord

goat

grandmother

your mother's or your father's mother

Grandmother Aho's House

I remember. . . .

I loved to visit Grandmother Aho. There was a big iron kettle outside her house. It caught the rainwater we used to wash our hair.

The kettle was much too heavy to move. I don't know where it came from, or how it got there. When I hit the kettle, it rang like a bell. I could feel the metal sing with my fingertips.

And I remember. . . .

Long ago when I was very little, Grandmother Aho took me into her barn. She showed me a box of bones. They were the bones of a horse called Little Red. Grandmother Aho said Little Red was the fastest horse in the world. Lots of horses raced Little Red. But Little Red always won.

Each time I visited Grandmother Aho, I would go to the barn and look at the bones. Later they were stolen. I never found out why she kept those bones or why someone wanted to steal them from her.

And I remember. . . .

Early one morning Grandmother Aho and I took a walk. A buffalo calf had just been born in the tall grass. It was red-orange and beautiful with new life. We watched the calf wobble to its feet.

But its mother saw us. She was afraid we would hurt her calf. So she bent her great dark head and charged.

Grandmother Aho grabbed my hand. We ran and ran and ran. It was spring. Our hearts were beating fast, and I knew just then what it was to be alive.

N. Scott Momaday

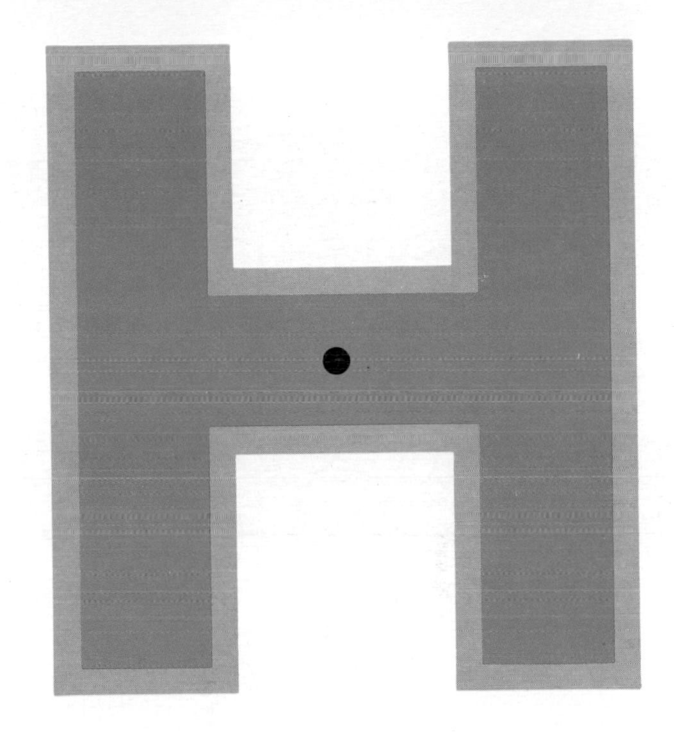

Look at the black dot in the H and count slowly to 20. Then look at the white part of the page and count to 20.

Do you see a red H with a blue border?

haircut

BLIT AND BLAT
WHERE DOES A LAMB GO TO GET A HAIRCUT?
TO THE BAA BAA SHOP.

hamburger

It is reported that Bill Wall ate 80 hamburgers in 3 hours. His friends tried to beat his record but they just couldn't ketchup.

Who is going to hand out the name tags?
Aren't we lucky that Mr. Fist is on hand to help us with the field trip?
That teacher has her hands full with that group of kids.
Let's give Mary Lou a hand. This trip was her idea.
Do you think someone made that by hand?
We'd better keep our hands off that.
hand

handsome

good-looking

The Lion and the Mouse

One day a lion, a quite handsome lion, was walking in the forest. Now the lion was feeling pretty good. So as he walked along, he hummed a feeling-pretty-good song.

"Dum, dee, dum-dum; doo, dee, doo-doo," he hummed to himself. Just as he was about to hum the next line, he spotted a small pond.

"Just what I need," the lion said. "A mirror." And he stopped and looked at himself in the water.

"My, my, my!" he said. "I am a handsome cat. I am indeed."

The lion was feeling very pleased with himself. He looked in the pond again and smiled.

"Such a handsome cat. The most handsome cat around, you might say."

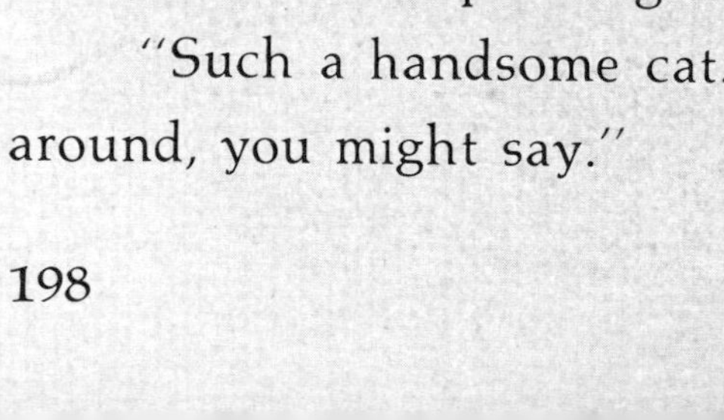

Just then a giraffe came galloping by. "I think I'll stop for a drink," she said.

When the lion saw the giraffe, he tried not to laugh.

"Look at you," the lion said. "Don't you wish you had a long, gold mane? Don't you wish you could look like me? You must be ever so sad. Let me ask you a question. Why aren't you as strong and big and handsome as I am?"

The giraffe thought to herself, "Who does he think he is? You can't even stop by the pond these days without running into some nut." The giraffe shook her head and walked away.

The lion stretched. He looked at his paws. "Mmm, such fine paws. Such beautiful long nails. They are so clean and sharp." While the lion was talking to himself, a hippopotamus came galumphing by.

"I think I'll take a swim," said the hippopotamus.

The lion saw the hippopotamus step into the mud. "Oh dear, I am sorry for you," said the lion. "Don't you wish you had paws like mine? I just don't understand. Why aren't you as clean and handsome as I am?"

The hippopotamus thought for a minute. "I don't know," he said. "And I don't care." Then he turned and galumphed away.

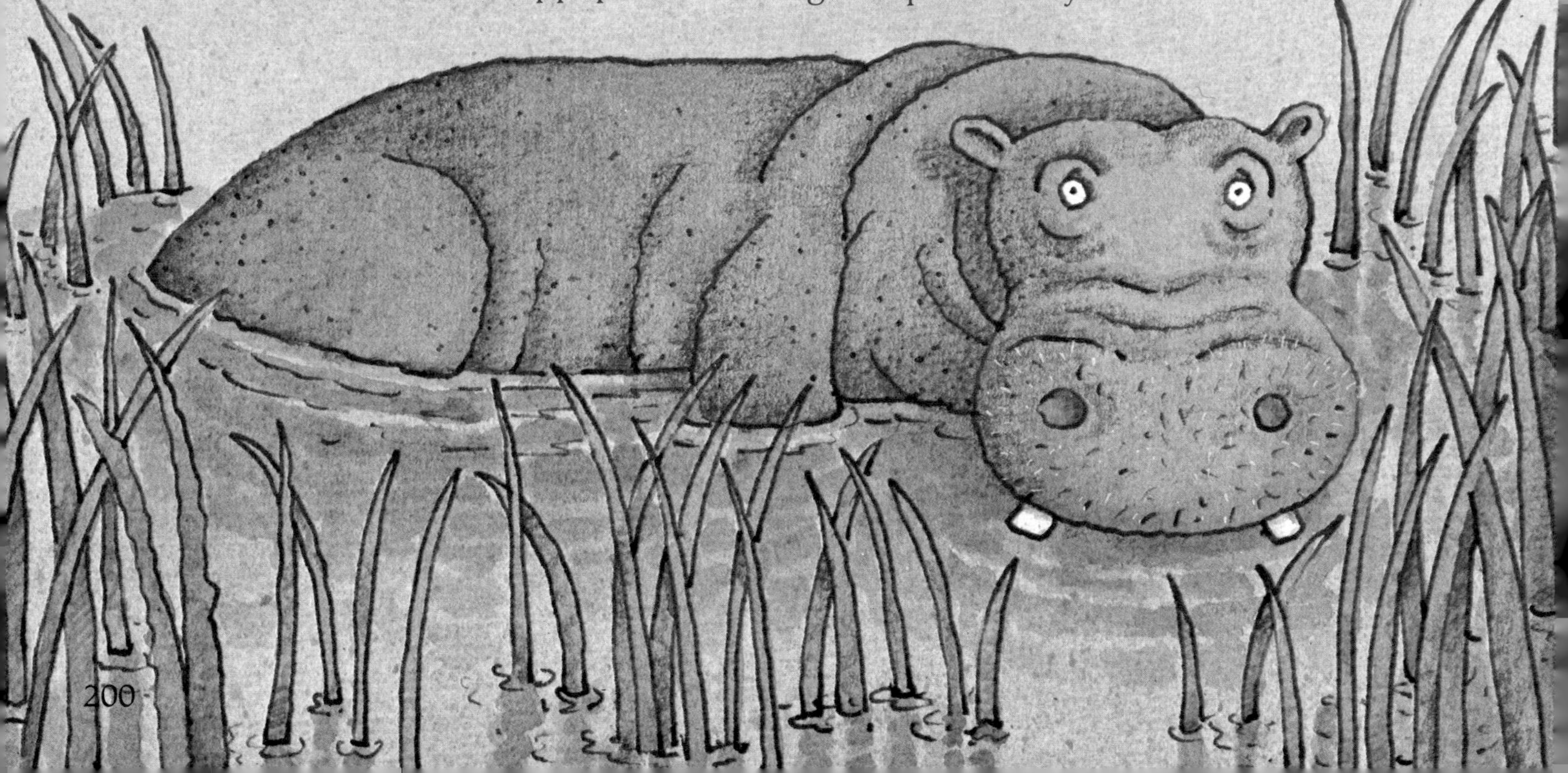

Just as the lion was having a sip of water, who should come trotting by but a wart hog.

When the lion saw her, he began to cry. "Oh, dear. What happened to you? Your skin is so gray. Have you been to a doctor? I am sure your skin should be soft and furry and gold like mine."

The wart hog was furious. "Doctor!" she snapped. "Gray! My skin is supposed to be gray. Leave me alone!"

"Oh, my," cried the lion. "I am so sorry. Please forgive me. But tell me—why aren't you as strong and big and gold and handsome as I am?"

The wart hog did not answer. She was so furious that she stomped off before the lion could say another word.

The lion shook his head. "What did I say that made her so mad?"

The lion sat by the pond all day and looked at himself. "I am so handsome," he said. "No wonder I am called the King of Beasts."

Late that afternoon, a little mouse scurried by. When the lion saw the mouse, he began to roar—roar with laughter, that is.

"I am sorry to laugh. But you are such a funny-looking thing. So tiny and gray. Just take a look at yourself."

The mouse looked in the pond. He saw his short, gray whiskers. Then he looked up at the lion's long, gold whiskers. He looked at his own little body. Then he looked at the lion's big, furry body. The mouse looked at his skinny, gray tail. Then he looked at the lion's thick, soft tail. The mouse looked at the lion. He tried to make a muscle. It was so small that he could not see a thing.

"Why aren't you as strong and big and handsome as I am?" said the lion.

The mouse squirmed.
Then he blushed.
At last he squeaked,
"Well, to tell the truth,
I've been sick lately."

Duncan Emrich

head

Use your head to solve this mystery.

Just Ring the Bell

It was late at night when the man arrived at the hotel. He walked slowly and looked very, very tired.

He put his bag down and asked the woman at the front desk, "May I please have a room for one night? I haven't had any sleep for two days. I am very tired."

The woman got a key and showed the man his room.

"Is there anything else, sir?" she asked politely.

"Yes. Please make sure that you wake me in the morning at six. It's very important," he said.

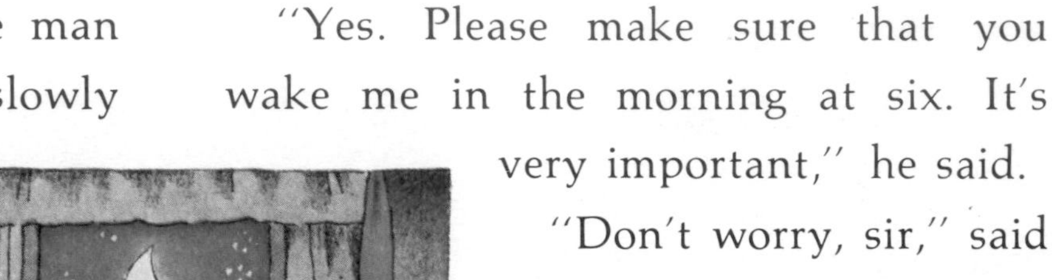

"Don't worry, sir," said the woman. "Just ring that bell by your bed, and I will come wake you."

"Thank you," said the man. "Good night."

Do you think the man got up on time?

Find the answer on page 334.

heat

heat is hot—cold it's not

The sand in the desert gets terribly hot.
And the heat on your feet
Is as hot
As a pot
Of hot water
Believe it or not.

heavy

If you carry something that is too heavy,
You will get tired.
Your
knees
will
bend,
And soon you will
drop
it!

help

Juma was very small for his age. He tried to play with the other boys, but they laughed at him. Juma was unhappy.

"Do not worry," said his uncle, Umtali. "Not all the animals in a herd are the same. Some must walk alone."

"Must I?" asked Juma.

"It is better to stay away when the herd will not have you," Umtali answered.

Juma took his uncle's advice. He began to spend time alone in the forest. At first he would sing and whistle. But then he was silent. He watched and listened to the wild animals around him. Each day Juma learned more about the animals. Soon they were no longer afraid of him.

One day Umtali said, "Walk with me, Juma, and tell me what you have learned."

"Many things, Uncle. I have learned how sometimes the weak animals stay away from the strong ones. The older zebras protect the young ones from the hungry lioness. The baboon never goes to the watering hole when the fierce leopard is there.

"Sometimes the weak and strong live together. A crocodile will let its bird friends sit on its head. The birds even walk into its open mouth, looking for food.

"But do the strong ever help the weak?" asked Juma.

"Yes, sometimes," said Umtali. His eyes grew wet with memories.

"I have seen a wounded elephant lifted on his feet by two others—one on each side holding him up."

"Where did they take him?" Juma asked excitedly. "To the elephants' burial ground?"

"Maybe." Umtali was quiet for a minute. "But no one has ever seen that place."

Juma and Umtali did not say much to each other as they walked

home. They were both thinking of the mysteries of the animals.

The next day Juma again went into the forest. He took a path off an old trail. It led to a sunny meadow that buzzed with the sound of grasshoppers. It was a hot day. Juma sat down to rest before the walk home. Soon he fell asleep.

Was he dreaming? Juma thought he felt something on his back. He froze. Then he opened his eyes. An elephant stood over him, blotting out the sky.

The elephant shifted his feet slowly. He threw up his trunk and smelled the air. He waved his ears back and forth. Then he picked Juma up in his trunk. Carefully, he put the boy on his head and began to walk.

Juma was frightened but curious. The elephant was old and thin. He moved slowly.

"What does he want with me?" Juma thought.

The elephant stumbled through the forest. He did not seem to know where he was going. He kept crashing into bushes and trees.

And then, at last, Juma knew what was wrong. The elephant was blind.

Juma understood. The Blind One wanted the boy to be his eyes. The old elephant needed Juma's help.

Gently Juma pushed the Blind One's head to show him where to go. It worked. So it was true. He was to be the elephant's eyes.

All day Juma helped the blind elephant. The elephant chose the trail, and Juma guided him along. It was dark when the old elephant stopped. He put Juma down. Juma tried to crawl away. But each time he tried, the great trunk pulled him back.

They traveled all the next day. It was late when they reached the hills. The ground was getting steeper.

The elephant moved more slowly.

The third morning they came to a river. Nearby, a waterfall splashed and tumbled.

Suddenly the Blind One seemed to get new strength. He stopped. Then, raising his trunk, he trumpeted. The sound echoed through the hills until it was lost. Gently, he picked Juma up with his trunk and put him on the ground. Juma did not move.

He watched the Blind One step into the river. At the waterfall the old elephant stopped. A rainbow of mist circled his wrinkled head.

Slowly, almost sadly, he raised his trunk again. One last time he drew in the smell of the land which had been his home for so long. Then, like a tired shadow, the old elephant walked through the waterfall and disappeared.

It took a few minutes before Juma realized he was alone. He felt that he had lost something old and wonderful.

As Juma turned to start home, he saw Umtali. His uncle was high on a rock above him. Umtali waved and hurried down to Juma.

"Are you all right? I was worried when you did not come back; so I followed your trail. Soon I knew where the elephant was taking you."

Juma understood. "This must be the elephants' burial ground."

"Yes," Umtali said. "I found it many years ago. But I told no one."

"But where did the old elephant go? What is behind the waterfall?"

"I do not know. That is the secret of the elephants. It is not for me to take it away from them."

"The old elephant trusted me to help him," Juma said. "I will keep his secret always." He looked at Umtali. "And the old elephant helped me, too, Uncle. He taught me to stand alone."

The years passed. Juma grew tall and straight as a spear. Only Juma knew that he had been the Blind One's eyes. But everyone knew that he had lived among the wild ones, and for this they respected him.

John Mansfield

hide and seek

Glen is It. Let's go!
The fence?
No. Those boards won't hide
me at all.
1-2-3-4-5
The shed?
No. Can't get inside.
The door's locked.
6-7-8-9-10
The tree?
No. Too close. Brad tried
that last time.
11-12-13-14-15
That box?
Yes. If it's upside
down, I'll fit.
1-2-3 on Brent
Tight squeeze.

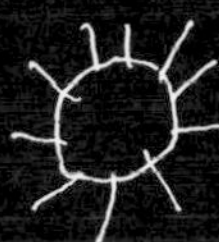

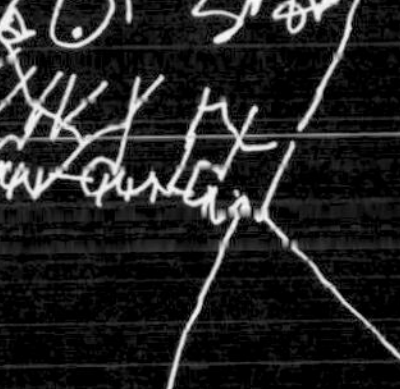

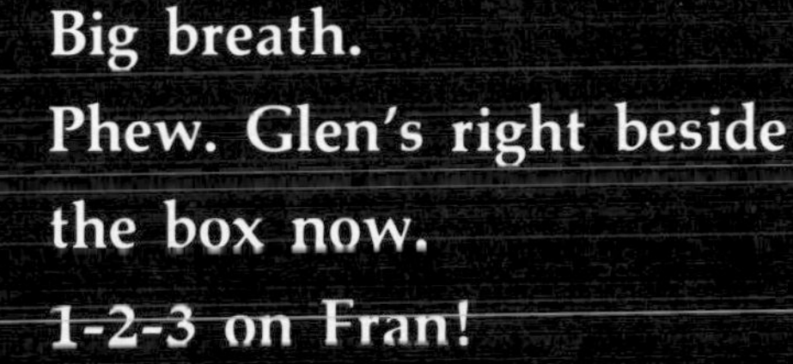

Oomph. And now outside
Glen's looking.
1-2-3 on Val!
Big breath.
Phew. Glen's right beside
the box now.
1-2-3 on Fran!
That's it.
Everyone's been spied
except me.
Who's It this time?
Wait!
Hey. Glen never tried
to find me.
1-2-3-4-5
Dumb game.
Yes. I don't like hide
and not seek.

hieroglyph

a picture that stands for a word

Picture writing is one of the oldest kinds of writing. People used pictures instead of letters. These pictures were called hieroglyphs. To write about a hand, a person would draw a hand. To write about a bird, a person would draw a bird. Early hieroglyphs were carved on stone tablets.

What kind of tool would you need to carve hieroglyphs on stone?

Why would it be hard to do your homework?

How would you correct a mistake?

Why would it be hard to store the stone tablets?

Which of these words would be easy to draw? *beautiful, arrow, dog, tomorrow, think, camel, boat*

Here are some hieroglyphs and the words they stand for.

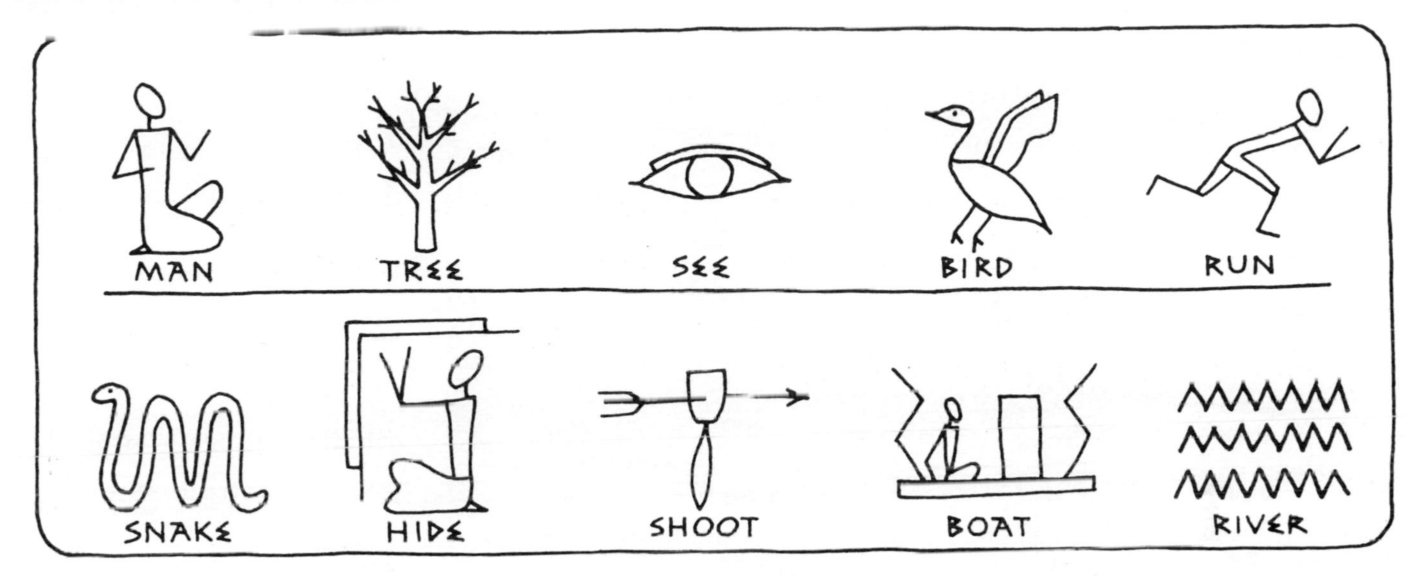

What story do you think these hieroglyphs tell?

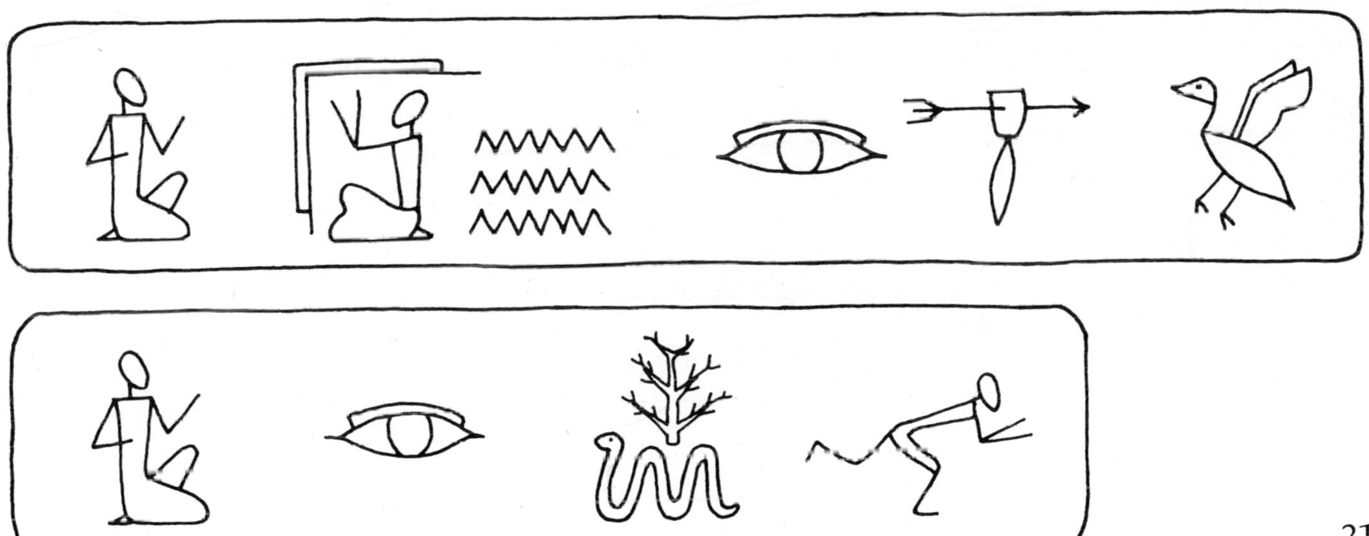

honeybee

the insect that makes the honey that is sold in stores

Bees are the only insects that make honey. They make it in a hive or bee house.

Cover fits over hive to keep out rain or snow.
Inner cover keeps bees from getting too warm or too cold.
Shallow super is needed to store extra honey.
Hive body is used by the queen to lay the eggs.
Bottom board allows the bees to enter the hive.
Hive stand has a board for bees to land on.

Beehives can be taken apart easily. Beekeepers can remove the honey without being stung and without killing any of the bees.

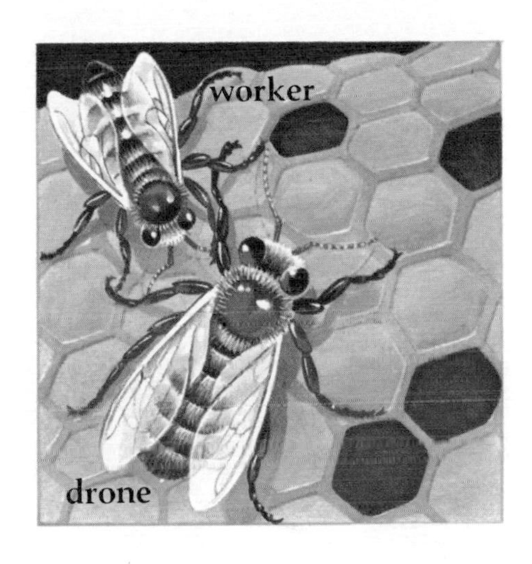

Three kinds of bees live in a hive. Each hive has one queen bee, a few hundred drones, and thousands of workers.

The queen bee is the largest. She is also the most important. She lays all the eggs. If the queen bee dies, the worker bees find a new queen right away. Without a queen, no more bees would be born in the hive.

A drone is a male bee. Drones do no work and cannot sting. Drones mate with the queen so she can lay eggs. The drones that mate with the queen die. All the other drones are pushed from the hive or killed by the worker bees.

The worker bees do the hard work of the hive. Workers clean the empty cells in the hive for the queen to lay eggs in. When the eggs hatch, workers take care of the baby bees.

The worker bees guard the hive against anything that tries to get in. They sting their enemies to drive them away. When a worker bee stings something, the bee dies. The worker bees also make wax. They use this wax to fill cracks in the hive. But the most important job the worker does is to make honey.

To make honey, the worker bees need flowers. A worker flies into a flower, sticks its long tongue inside, and sucks out the nectar. This sweet juice is what the workers use to make the honey. The bees eat the honey and feed it to the young bees. But they store most of the honey in cells in the hive.

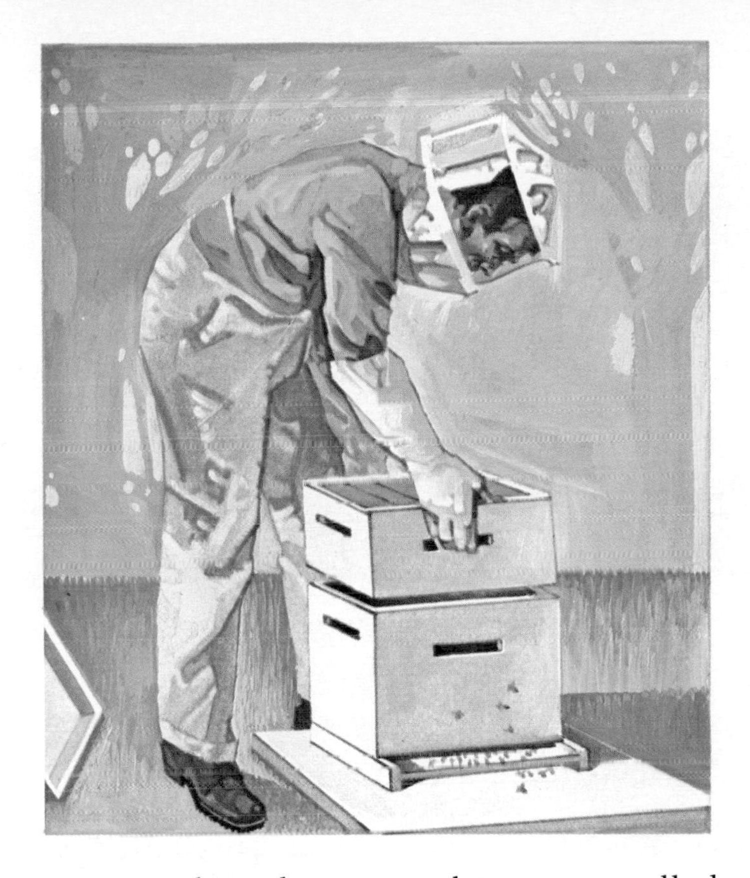

People who raise bees are called beekeepers. The beekeeper takes some honey from the hive and puts it in jars to sell. The rest of the honey is left in the hive, so the bees will always have enough to eat.

hummingbird

The ruby-throated hummingbird
Is hardly bigger than this

WORD.

Jack Prelutsky

I

The trees ask me,
And the sky,
And the sea asks me
Who am I?

The grass asks me,
And the sand,
And the rocks ask me
Who I am.

The wind tells me
At nightfall,
And the rain tells me
Someone small.

Someone small
Someone small
But a piece of
it
all.

Felice Holman

iceberg

a large mass of ice floating in the sea

To find out what happens when a ship hits an iceberg, make this ship. (You will need a rectangular piece of paper.) Then turn the page and read "The Ballad of Captain Blow."

1. Fold rectangle in half from top to bottom.

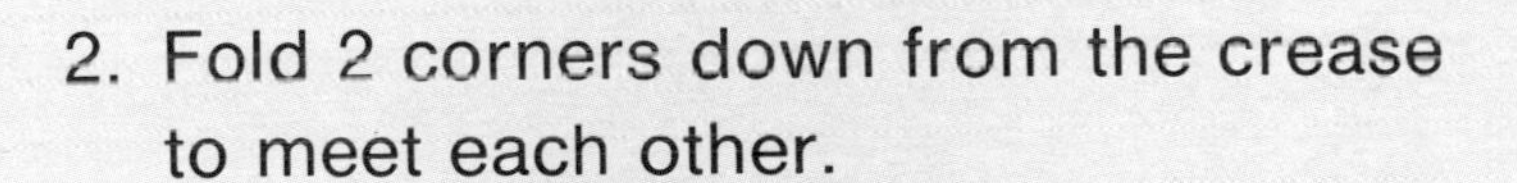

2. Fold 2 corners down from the crease to meet each other.

3. Fold up the bottoms, one on each side, so you have a hat.

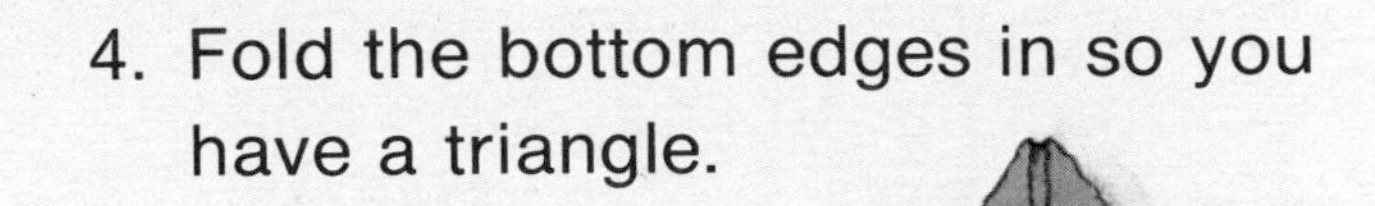

4. Fold the bottom edges in so you have a triangle.

5. Pull out the sides so the bottom points of the triangle come together, and you have a square.

6. Fold up the 2 bottom corners, one on each side, to make another triangle.

7. With this triangle repeat step 5 so you have another square.

8. With the crease in your square running up and down, grasp the 2 points of the square which open out and pull.

9. Flatten the paper and you have a boat.

The Ballad of Captain Blow and the Iceberg

Captain Blow had sailed his ship
For many a day and night.
He reached the sea of ice and said,
"Oh! Look! There's land in sight."

"No," said the sailors, shaking with fear.
"That's an iceberg up ahead.
We really must go slow or BUMP,
Oh! We will all be dead!"

The captain tried to turn the ship,
But it was much too late.
The bow sank slowly in the sea.
Oh! What would be their fate?

Tear off the front corner of the ship.

The sailors jumped onto the ice,
But not brave Captain Blow.
He bumped another iceberg hard.
Oh! The stern was next to go.

Tear off the back corner of the ship.

And then the sail came tumbling down.
It fell into the sea.
Brave Captain Blow stayed right on board.
"Oh! I won't leave," said he.

Tear off the center triangle.

All that was left of Captain Blow
Was his shirt that floated by.
The sailors watched, then shouted out,
"Oh! Captain Blow, good-bye!"

Unfold the paper carefully and you'll find the shirt.

incident

an event or happening

It had taken two thousand workers two years to build the largest and most modern steamship the world had ever seen. But by 1912, the *Titanic* was ready to cross the Atlantic Ocean from England to New York City.

The *Titanic* was like a floating hotel. It had dining rooms, a ballroom, and library. It had a gym, a swimming pool, and a playroom for children. It even had a hospital with an operating room. The cabins, or bedrooms, had fine furniture and were like the fanciest rooms in any hotel on land. There were special rooms for the servants of rich passengers. There was even a kennel for pets.

People from all over the world sailed on the first voyage of the *Titanic*. They wanted to be the first to cross the ocean on the most luxurious ship of that time.

The 2200 passengers spent their first days at sea just trying to find their way around the huge ship. This was quite a job because the *Titanic* was as long as four city blocks and as tall as a five-story building.

The passengers dined on fine food prepared by the ship's cooks. They danced in the elegant ballroom to the music of a large band. People played tennis on deck and swam in the pool. Women had their hair fixed in the beauty shop. Men visited the barbers for their morning shave. Games and parties were planned for the children, but they also enjoyed just playing hide and seek on the enormous ship. And everyone talked about the *Titanic* and about how it was the safest and most beautiful ship they had ever seen.

The first five days at sea were wonderful. But on the fifth night a terrible incident happened. It was almost midnight. Most of the passengers and crew were in bed. Suddenly some passengers felt a strange bump. It seemed to come from the bottom of the *Titanic*. Most people went back to sleep, but those who were curious hurried out on deck.

From there the passengers could see icebergs floating nearby. Because chips of ice were on the deck, some people guessed that the *Titanic* had hit an iceberg. But they were not

worried because they were sure that nothing could hurt the great ship.

They were wrong. The bump was much worse than anyone imagined. The *Titanic* had hit an iceberg, and the iceberg had ripped a hole in one side of the ship. No one knew it yet, but water was rushing through that hole and into the bottom of the great ship.

The captain was one of the first to know that the *Titanic* was in trouble. Quickly he ordered the crew to wake all the passengers and to get the lifeboats ready. The crew raced through the ship. They directed the passengers to put on their life jackets and to hurry to the deck.

Many passengers didn't bother getting dressed. They just put the life jackets on over their pajamas. Quickly they scrambled out on deck. Most people still had no idea that the great ship had been damaged.

The crew shouted for the men to stand back and for the women and children to get into the lifeboats first. Many people refused. They could not believe that the most powerful ship in the world was going to sink. Surely, they thought, the giant *Titanic* would be safer than the tiny lifeboats that were being lowered into the dark, icy ocean.

Water was creeping higher and higher inside the ship. It started to come through the deck where the passengers were standing. At last everyone realized that the ship was going down. Frantically, they pushed and shoved their way toward the lifeboats.

Husbands kissed their wives good-bye and told them not to worry. Fathers hugged their children and said they would get into other lifeboats later. But they were wrong. Most of the families were never together again. The men never had a chance to get into lifeboats at all. For there were only twenty lifeboats on the *Titanic*, and twenty lifeboats were not enough to carry 2200 people.

When the last lifeboat had been lowered, the captain shouted for the remaining passengers to jump overboard. Leaping from the deck of

the *Titanic* was like jumping off a high cliff. Yet it was the only chance for people to save themselves. They knew they would surely die if they didn't jump. So they leaped into the cold, dark ocean.

The people in the lifeboats could hear the cries and screams of their friends and loved ones in the icy water, but nothing could be done to help. The lifeboats were already too crowded. They would sink under the weight of more people. There was no way to save the hundreds of drowning people.

Through the darkness, the people in the lifeboats and those in the water could see that the *Titanic* was sinking quickly. The front half of the ship was now underwater. The back half was sticking straight up in the air. Helplessly the people watched the *Titanic* sink deeper into the ocean. In less than two and a half hours, the greatest ship in the world was gone forever.

It was a terrible lesson to learn. For although the *Titanic* was the most modern ship of its day, it was not carrying enough simple lifeboats for all its passengers. Fifteen hundred people died in one of the worst sea disasters of all time.

A Play in Three Acts

Franklin Stein:	a quiet boy who loves to invent things
Gertrude Stein:	Franklin's mother
Ine Stein:	Franklin's father
Phyllis Stein:	Franklin's sister
Sarah Hairball:	a nervous person
Niece Clarice:	Sarah Hairball's niece
La Donna Metz:	an opera singer
Walt N. Peffer:	one of the Five Peffers who live downstairs
Landlord Twitch:	a man who doesn't like pets
Elizabeth:	a quiet girl who loves to invent things
Fred:	Franklin's invention

The Steins' living room. Gertrude is reading the paper. Ine and Phyllis are playing checkers. Footstools are all around the room.

Franklin: *offstage* Bang! Bang! Bang!

Gertrude Stein: Franklin's mother
Franklin Stein! What in the world are you doing up there? You've been hammering and hammering, night and day for a week. What are you inventing this time?

Franklin: Bang!

Ine Stein: Franklin's father
I don't know what he's doing, but the last time Franklin invented something, all my shoes were missing. I just hope this invention doesn't have sixteen feet like the last one.

Gertrude Stein: Yes, I hope he's not making any more footstools. I don't have any shoes left either.
Franklin's mother

Phyllis Stein: Oh that dumb Franklin! He probably doesn't even know what he's making.
Franklin's sister

Franklin: Bang! Bang! Bang!

Gertrude Stein: Franklin! Come downstairs. It's time to go to the pet show.

Phyllis Stein: Don't worry. He'll come.
Franklin's sister

Franklin: Bang! Bang! Bang!

Gertrude Stein: But I am worried. All Franklin does is invent things. He never spends any time with his friends.

Phyllis Stein: What friends? He doesn't have any friends.

Ine Stein: Don't worry, dear. I'm sure Franklin will be just fine. By the way, do you know where my tie is?
Franklin's father

Franklin:	Bang! Bang! Bang!
Gertrude Stein:	Your tie is probably with my potato masher. That's been missing for a week, too.
Franklin:	Bang! Bang! Bang!
Ine Stein:	Franklin! Stop that racket and come down here!
Phyllis Stein:	Well, you asked for it. Here he comes, and look at that! What dumb thing have you made this time, Franklin?
Franklin: *entering room*	This is Fred.
Gertrude Stein:	That's nice, dear. What is Fred?
Franklin:	Fred's my friend.
Phyllis Stein:	What a dumb friend!
Ine Stein:	Don't bring that junk in here.

Franklin: Don't listen to them, Fred. Let's go. We'll be late.

Franklin's front yard. Some of Franklin's neighbors are in the yard. Sarah Hairball and Niece Clarice are hiding behind some bushes. They are peeking out at Franklin and Fred. Walt N. Peffer is digging for worms. Landlord Twitch is waiting to talk to Franklin. Elizabeth is looking out a window.

Sarah Hairball: Look, Niece Clarice. Who's that with Franklin? It must be a robber! Niece Clarice, call the police!

Niece Clarice: Don't worry, Auntie Hairball. It's not a robber. It's one of Franklin's friends.

Sarah Hairball: Silly goose! Franklin doesn't have any friends. It *must* be a robber. Quick, Niece Clarice! Call the police!

Franklin: Good morning, Ms. Hairball. Hi, Niece Clarice. What are you doing hiding in the bushes?

Niece Clarice:	We're trying to catch Skeet, our parakeet. Hey Franklin, who is that with you?
Franklin:	It's Fred.
Sarah Hairball:	A likely story! It's a robber, I tell you. And that Stein boy is helping him.
Clarice:	But Auntie Hairball . . .
Franklin: *walking away*	Come on, Fred. Never mind them. Let's go. We'll be late. Hi, Walt.
Walt N. Peffer: *looking up*	Hi, Franklin. Yuk! What is that?
Franklin:	It's Fred.
Walt N. Peffer:	He's weird, Franklin. And so are you. How come you are always so weird?
Franklin:	How come you are always digging for worms? Come on, Fred. Never mind him. Hurry up. We'll be late.

Walt N. Peffer: *shaking his head*	Weird.
Franklin: *bumping into Landlord Twitch*	Good morning, Mr. Twitch.
Landlord Twitch: *twitching*	Don't you good morning me, Franklin Stein. If I've told you once, I've told you twice: no pets allowed.
Franklin:	But, Mr. Twitch . . .
Landlord Twitch: *twitching*	Don't you talk back to me, Franklin. I've had enough of your back talk. I guess I'll just have to speak to your parents again. Now shoo! Get away from here. And take that, that disgusting thing with you! Tch, tch, tch.
Franklin:	Come on, Fred. Never mind him. Hurry up. We'll be late.

The neighborhood pet show. Franklin's neighbors are standing in a line with their pets. Sarah Hairball and Niece Clarice have found Skeet, their parakeet. Walt N. Peffer has a can of worms. Phyllis Stein has a mouse in a shoe box. Elizabeth has a turtle. Franklin is standing at the end of the line with Fred. His parents are watching as La Donna Metz judges the contest.

La Donna Metz: Welcome, welcome, my little dumplings, parents, and friends, to our second annual neighborhood pet show. How lovely to see you here, my little pumpernickels. Now I shall look at each of your pets and award this year's prize: a blue ribbon and three free singing lessons with me. ♫ Eee-ah ♫ Eee-ah ♫

Sarah Hairball:	One of us better win, Niece Clarice. We need those singing lessons. We must learn to scream loudly enough to call the police.
La Donna Metz:	Now, now, what do we have here? Ah-ah! A lovely little bird. It reminds me of an opera. Let me sing a little of it for you. Pa-pa-pa-pa-pa-pa-pa-gena. Pa-pa-gena
Sarah Hairball:	This is a pet show, not an opera. Stop singing and give me my prize!
La Donna Metz:	Ah-ah. Ah-ah. One moment, Ms. Hairball. I must look at *all* the pets before awarding the prize.
Niece Clarice:	Don't worry, Auntie Hairball. We'll win.
La Donna Metz:	Oh-oh! What do we have here, Walt N. Peffer? Worms! Worms! Worms remind me of a famous opera. Let me sing some of it for you.

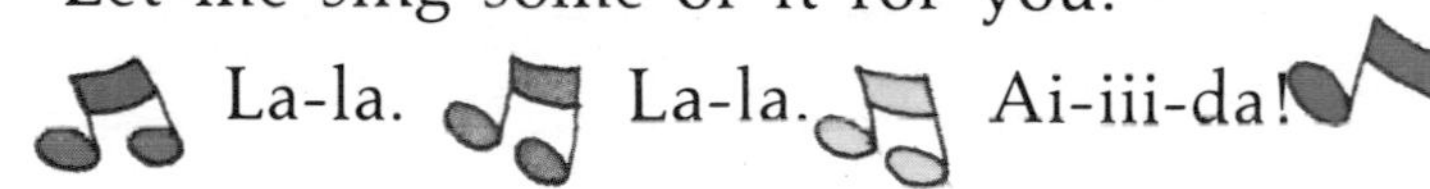

La-la. La-la. Ai-iii-da!

Walt N. Peffer:	Please be quiet, La Donna. You're scaring my worms.
La Donna Metz:	Ah-ah. What is this, Phyllis, my precious little frankfurter? A mouse? What a nasty little creature. But it does remind me of an opera. I'll just sing a little of it for you. Nibble, nibble mousie. Who's nibbling at my housie?
Phyllis Stein:	Oh, how gross! I'm not coming next year. This is really dumb!
La Donna Metz: *to Elizabeth*	Ah-ha! Ah-ha. A turtle. How wonderful. Its shell is like armor. It reminds me of the opera.
Elizabeth:	Oh, no. Here we go again.
La Donna Metz: *to Franklin*	Ea-ah. Valkyrie. Ea-ah. Valkyrie. Now what do we have here? Oo-la-la! Oo-la-la! Franklin, what a fantastic pet.

Phyllis Stein: Fantastic? That thing is dumb. Dumb and ugly!

Franklin: It's not ugly. It's Fred.

Elizabeth:	Fred is beautiful.
La Donna Metz:	Elizabeth is right. Franklin's pet is original! Creative! Artistic! Superb!
Franklin:	Really. It was nothing.
La Donna Metz:	Nothing? Nothing, you say. Well, you have the most unusual pet here. And now you have a blue ribbon to prove it. Franklin, you win the first prize.
Gertrude Stein:	Ine, aren't you proud of our little Franklin?
Ine Stein:	Very proud, Gertrude, very proud. But Franklin, I'd really like to have my tie back.
Phyllis:	Yeah, big shot. And the dumb potato masher, too. I hate lumpy mashed potatoes.
Elizabeth:	Phyllis, you're a lumpy mashed potato! Come on, Franklin. I've got my mini-bike. Let's get out of here.
Franklin:	O.K. Hey, did you make that mini-bike, Elizabeth?

Elizabeth:	Yes, I like to invent things, too. Come on, let's go.
Franklin:	Can I bring Fred along?
Elizabeth:	Of course! He's our friend, isn't he?

Ellen Raskin

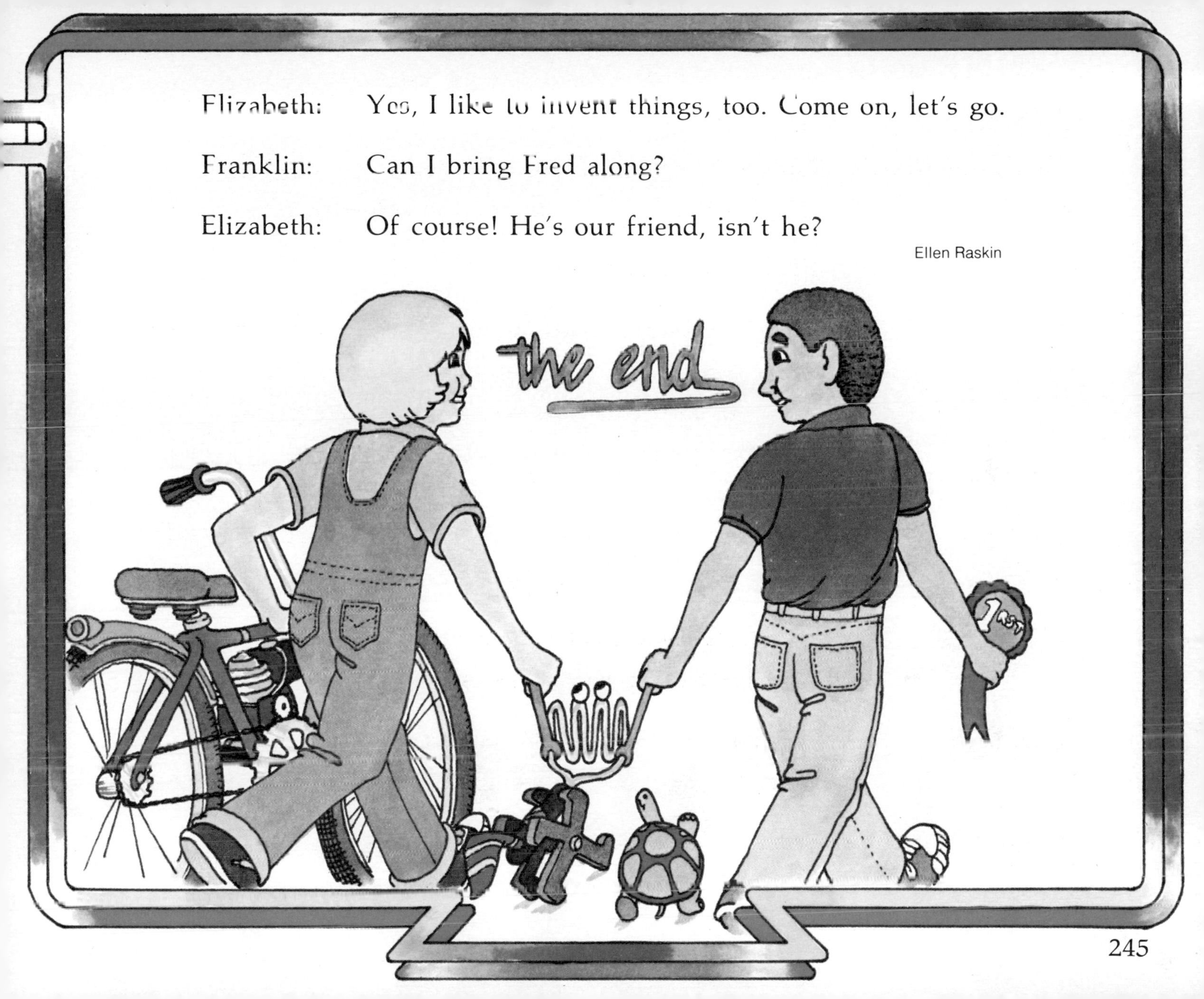

invisible

If something is invisible, you can't see it.

This is QX 10. This is QX 10 speaking. QX 10 is ready to report from Starship 563. Stardate 2630.

This is QX 10 in Starship 563. The starship is over the planet. The screening button is turned on, and we are invisible. Repeat: Starship 563 is invisible. The creatures on the planet can now be watched. Stand by for a description.

Each creature has a soft body without a shell. Four feelers are attached to the body.

Two feelers dangle from the upper part of the body. The other two feelers are on the lower part of the body. They help the body move around.

At the end of each feeler are five wigglers. None of the wigglers is furry. Are these wigglers dangerous? Please advise.

These creatures have only one head. And only half the head has fur. On each side of the head, a flap grows under the fur. Are these flaps antennae? Please advise.

The part of the head that is not covered with fur has an opening in it. Hard, sharp, white things grow inside the opening.

Above this opening is something that sticks out from the head. It has two holes in the bottom of it. What is it used for? Please advise.

Near the top of the head are two round moving spots. The spots are white with colored centers. Every few seconds a flap comes down and covers each spot. Little hairs curl out of the flap. Fur grows in a line above each moving spot. Are these spots dangerous? Please advise.

Stand by for a picture of these creatures transmitted over the Draw-a-thon. No direct contact will be made with the creatures until further instructions for this mission are received.

Please advise.

Over and out,

QX 10, Starship 563, Stardate 2630.

Island

Like "I" alone from "We,"

Is land

Alone at sea.

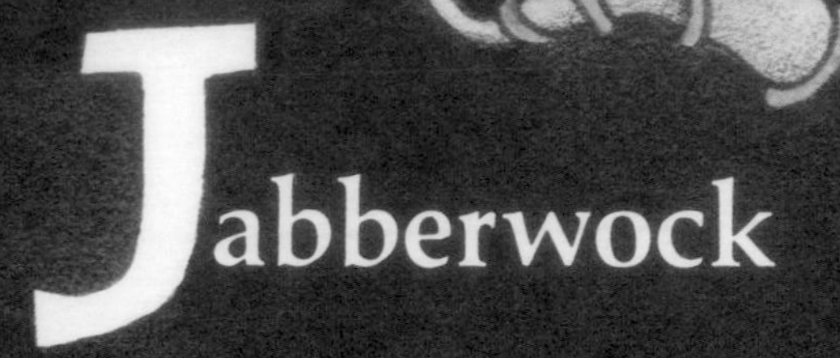

Jabberwock

Beware the Jabberwock, my son!
The jaws that bite, the claws that catch!
Beware the Jubjub bird, and shun
The frumious Bandersnatch!

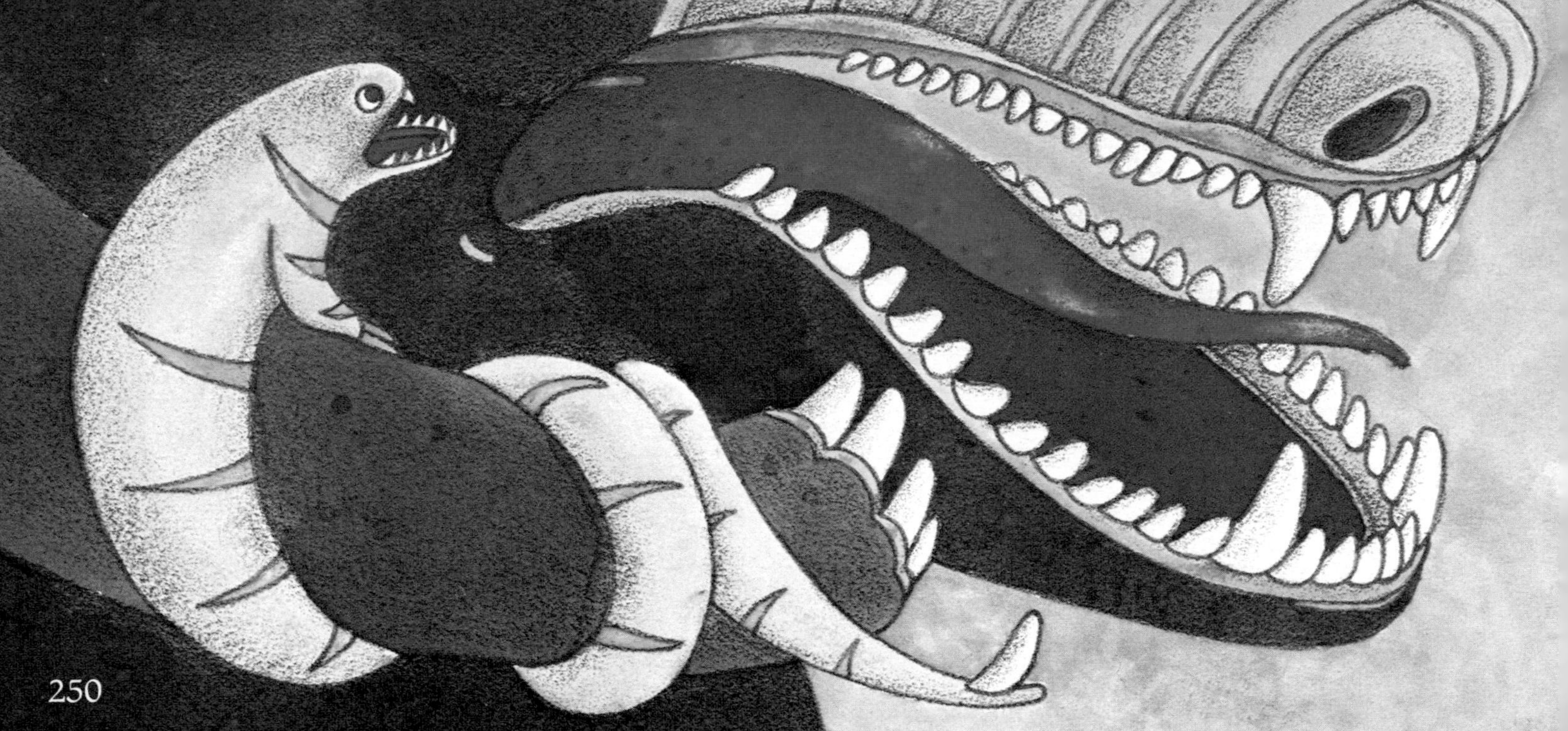

jack

a jack-o-lantern

a jack in a deck of cards

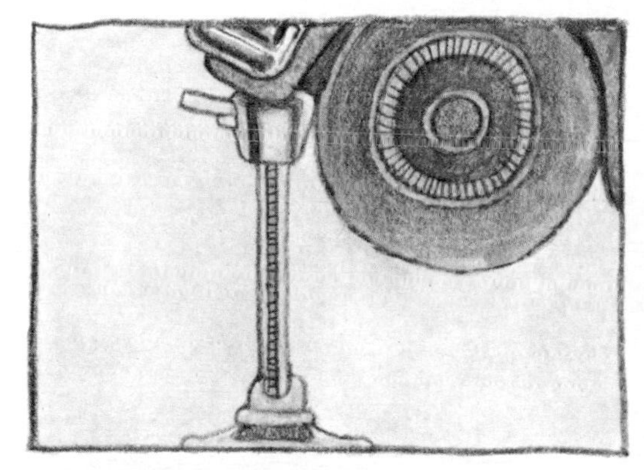

a jack used for lifting something heavy

the name of the boy in the beanstalk

a jack-in-the-box

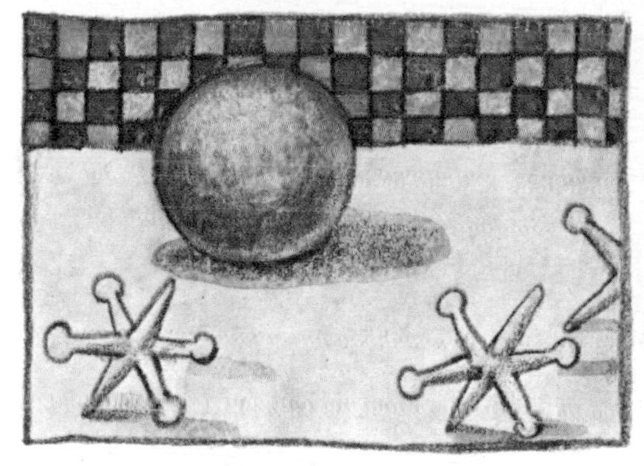

a game of jacks

Japan

a country made up of islands
in the Pacific Ocean

Hundreds of years ago in Japan, there were deep-sea divers called *ama*. In Japanese, *ama* means "girl of the sea." The *ama* would dive far beneath the surface of the ocean in search of oysters that held precious pearls. Each *ama* learned her skill from her mother and her grandmother who had been divers before her. It was a special tradition passed down from mother to daughter, generation after generation.

A young girl learned to dive when she was about eleven years of age. Her mother taught her how deep to dive and where to look for oysters. Her mother also taught her how to hold her breath underwater without getting too tired. At first a girl dived in water that was only six feet deep. When she was older and knew how to

hold her breath in a certain way, she could dive in deeper water. With lots of practice, she learned to hold her breath for as long as two or three minutes. Then she could dive to the ocean floor where she would cut the hard-shelled oysters away from the rocks. The work was dangerous because sharks often swam in the same waters. For this reason, the *ama* wore white. They believed that sharks were afraid of anything that was white.

Today, as in times past, young girls are taught to dive. Grandmothers and mothers still swim beneath the surface of the ocean beside the younger *ama.* They still dive for oysters. But they no longer have to *search* for oysters with pearls in them. Today, there is an easier way. Instead of searching for pearls in oysters, the Japanese grow, or "culture," pearls.

A way to grow pearls was discovered about eighty years ago by a man named Kokichi Mikimoto. He found that when a grain of sand was placed inside an oyster, it irritated, or bothered, the soft body of the oyster. So the oyster covered it with a special smooth coating. When the grain of sand was coated, it no longer bothered the oyster. After three years of coating the sand, the oyster formed a beautiful pearl.

Mikimoto learned the oyster's secret only after he had spent many years experimenting. At first, he tried putting sand inside 10,000 oysters. But when he opened them all, there were no pearls. Mikimoto then tried getting oysters to form pearls around bits of wax, copper, and glass. Nothing worked. Finally Mikimoto again tried putting grains of sand in the oysters. This time he placed the grain so far inside the oyster's shell that it couldn't be pushed out. It worked, and Mikimoto became famous all over the world for discovering how to culture pearls.

Kokichi Mikimoto became known as the Pearl King. He could make millions of oysters form millions of pearls. No longer were pearls so rare that only the *ama* could find them. No longer were pearls so expensive that only the rich could buy them.

Today there are pearl farms in

Kokichi Mikimoto

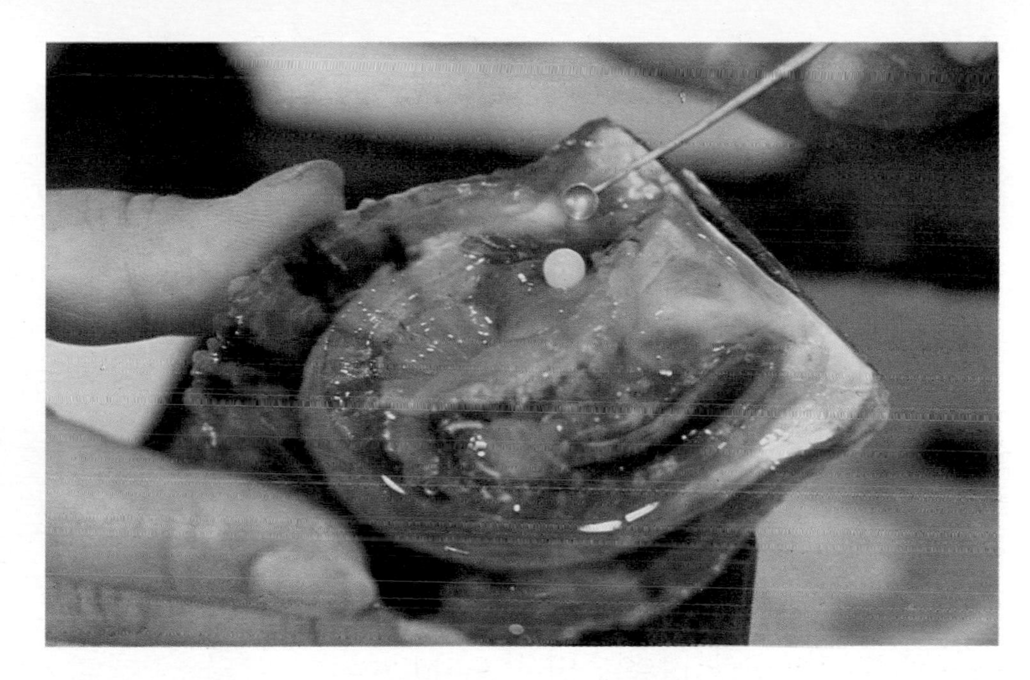

Japan. *Ama* dive for oysters that are about two or three years old. Grains of sand are placed inside oysters. Then the oysters are put back in the water. After three years the oysters are gathered and the pearls removed. Oysters live from ten to twelve years. They form the most beautiful pearls when they are five to six years old.

Millions of cultured pearls are made by the oysters that the *ama* bring up from the ocean floor. Although the *ama* don't search for pearls as they did long ago, the women are still very important. They dive to gather the live oysters that one day will form some of the world's most beautiful gems.

jinni

a magical creature who can grant wishes

Jo and the Jinni

There was a field behind Jo's house. Beyond it was a brook. Beside the brook were lots of big rocks. It was Jo's favorite place. She could pretend that the rocks were all sorts of things—ships, bad guys, horses.

Jo climbed up on a rock. "Ship ahoy!" she called. "Pirates!"

A voice behind her said, "Goodness me. You don't mean it!"

Jo whirled around. Leaning against a tree was a fat, little man. He was hardly bigger than Jo.

"I really am surprised about the pirates," the little man said. "I haven't seen any around here in weeks."

"In weeks?" Jo gulped. "You mean there *are* pirates around here?"

"Well, maybe it's been a little longer than weeks. A few years, I guess. A few hundred years." The man chuckled. "I'm afraid I sometimes get mixed up about time."

"You mean you saw pirates here hundreds of years ago?" Jo asked.

"Oh, yes. I saw them when they lived here. I don't see them now, of course. They don't live here anymore." Then he laughed.

"Gosh! But you must be—" Jo had started to say "very old." But she thought it might be rude. So she said, "You must have lived here a long time."

"Indeed I have," the little man said, twirling around. "But now let's get down to business. What's your wish?"

"My wish?" Jo asked.

"Yes, of course," the little man said. "Oh, dear me, I completely forgot."

Suddenly he looked very serious. He bowed. "I am the Jinni of the Rocks. I can make any wish come true for you. What is your command?"

Now, the only jinni Jo had ever heard of was in a fairy tale. That jinni had lived in a magic lamp.

Jo had never expected anything like this to happen to her.

"You're really a jinni?" Jo asked.

"Of course. What did you think I was—a fairy godmother?" He laughed. "Now, what is your wish?"

Jo knew exactly what she wanted. She wanted a girl to play with. She loved her three brothers, but she wanted someone like herself to talk to and share with.

"I'd like a friend—a girlfriend," Jo said.

"Of course. It's more fun to pretend when you play with a friend," said the jinni. "See? I made a little poem. Now then, what is your second wish?"

"I get another one?" Jo asked.

"Of course!" said the jinni.

Jo thought and thought. She'd already asked for what she wanted most.

"Well," she said slowly, "I guess I'd like to stay home from school tomorrow."

"Fine, fine." Then the jinni raised his hat and disappeared.

Jo didn't tell anyone about the Jinni of the Rocks. It seemed peculiar to her to have met him. She knew it would seem peculiar to everyone else.

The next morning Jo felt a little

strange. She looked in the mirror.

"Yow!" she yelled.

Jo's mother came running into the room.

"Mama! Look, I've got a terrible disease!" Jo cried.

"Don't worry, Josefina, it's just chicken pox," said her mother calmly.

By the following Saturday, all but two spots were gone. Right after breakfast, Jo ran to the rocks.

Feeling a little silly she called, "Hey, jinni!"

"Here I am," he said, bowing.

"I had chicken pox," Jo said.

"Yes. Wasn't I clever? You missed a whole week of school."

"I know," Jo said. "I missed the play. I didn't get to be a turtle."

"A turtle? I can turn you into a turtle if you wish," he said.

"No. No. I don't want you to turn me into a *real* turtle," said Jo. "It's all right, really. Forget it. I was just wondering about my first wish."

"Yes, of course," said the jinni. "These things aren't easy, you know. Friends don't come out of nowhere." The jinni laughed. "I need a little more time."

"Time?" Jo felt uneasy. She remembered how mixed up the jinni could get about time. It might take a hundred years.

"Now what's your third wish?" he asked. "Everyone gets three, you know."

Jo thought and thought. Suddenly she said, "I know! A magic lamp!"

The jinni disappeared. Where he had been standing was a lamp.

Josefina picked up the lamp. It wasn't quite what she had imagined. It looked like an ordinary lamp with a long cord and a plug. But she decided to give it a try.

She rubbed the lamp and asked for a piece of chocolate cake. Nothing happened.

"Maybe you have to plug it in," she thought.

But at home the lamp didn't work either.

The next day Jo went back to the rocks. The jinni was already there.

"How do you like your magic lamp?" asked the jinni.

"It doesn't work," said Jo.

"That's odd. All you have to do is plug it in, and it's supposed to light," said the jinni.

It's supposed to light?" Jo asked. "Is that what's magic about it? All lamps work like that."

"You're kidding," the jinni said. "You mean you don't need matches or oil?"

"No, we don't use lamps like that anymore," Jo said.

"Oh, I see. Then you don't really need me. That wish didn't work out very well." The jinni looked sad. "But, there's still the most important wish to come—a friend," he said. "Now, here's a little riddle for you to figure out:

Take a dish and knock at the door.

You'll see something for all four."

Jo was so busy trying to figure out the riddle, she didn't even see the jinni disappear.

"What dish? What door? Four what?" thought Jo.

The next few days went slowly. Jo kept watching doors and dishes. But nothing unusual happened.

On Thursday, when Jo came home from school, there was a moving van parked down the block. This was unusual. Jo was excited. She stood outside and watched the movers carry in furniture. Then she saw a car pull up.

"Mama! They're here," yelled Jo.

Jo's mother and brothers came outside to watch, too.

First a man got out of the car. A woman and three boys got out next.

Jo turned and started to walk away. She felt as if she were going to cry.

"Where are you going?" her mother called.

"To the rocks," she said in a choked voice.

"Don't stay too long," her mother said sadly.

Jo ran across the field to the rocks.

"Jinni!" she called angrily. But the jinni did not appear. "Jinni, your magic is no good."

Jo sat down. "What a swell bunch of wishes," she thought. "Chicken pox. A plain old lamp. And three more boys."

It was time for dinner when Jo got back.

"Could you do me a favor?" said her mother as Jo walked in. "Could you take this casserole over to our new neighbors?"

"Oh, Mom. Can't one of the boys do it?" Jo asked.

"I wish you would," said her mother, smiling.

Jo got the casserole dish and went down the street.

She knocked at the door. A man answered.

"Hi there," he said.

"Hi," said Jo. "My mother sent this over."

"Thanks very much. Won't you come in?" said the man.

Jo started to say, "No, thanks."

But suddenly she remembered:

Take a dish and knock at the door.

You'll see something for all four.

"What's your name?" the man asked as Jo walked in.

"Jo," she said.

He smiled. "Somebody in this house will be mighty glad to see you, Jo. Hey, Terry," the man called upstairs.

A girl about Jo's age came running down.

"Hi! Wow! Am I glad to see you," said Terry. "My grandmother drove me over a little while ago. But my brothers said they only saw boys at your house."

"Well, I thought the same thing about your house," said Jo.

Both girls laughed. "Come on up," Terry said. Jo followed her upstairs. "Brothers can be great," Terry continued. "But there are times when you need. . . ."

"I know exactly what you mean," Jo said.

Anita Feagles

jitters

The children at Main Street School
tell us what jitters are.

“what you get when you have to say a long poem all by yourself”

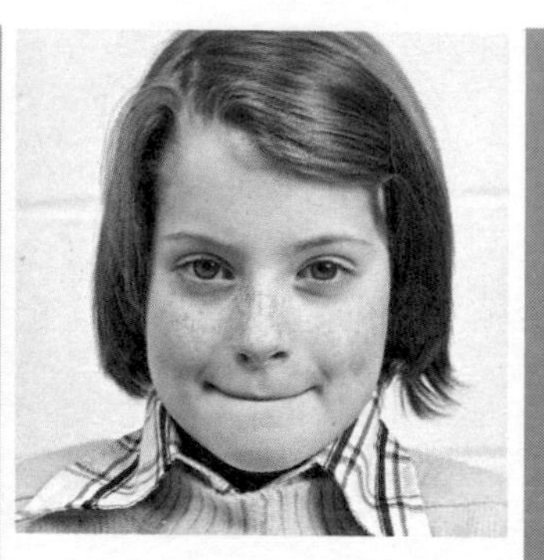

“what you get the day before school starts”

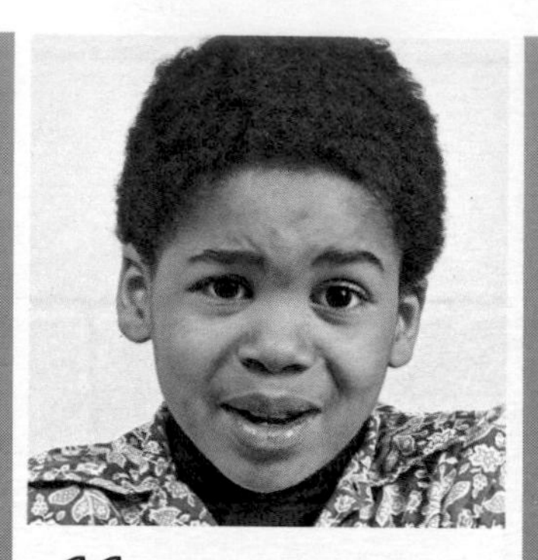

“what you get when you have to tell your dad that you broke your new bike”

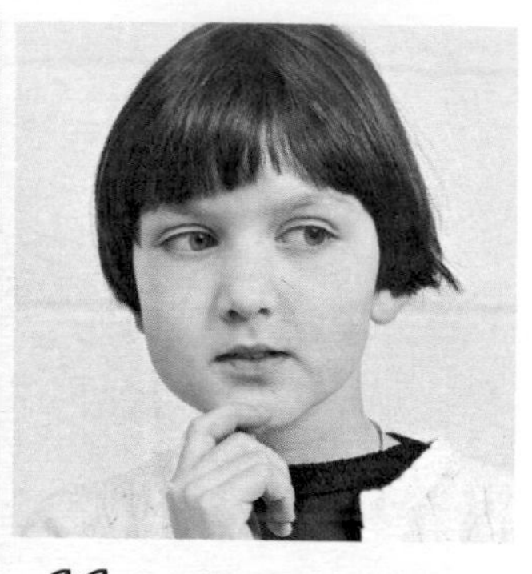

“what you get when your teacher asks you a question, and you don’t know the answer”

Everybody gets the jitters sometimes.

jokel

a jackal joke

If you tickle
A jackal,
You'd better be careful.
For the jackal
Will giggle
And then he will cackle.
His belly will jiggle.
His toes will all wiggle.
He'll roll on the ground on his backel,
That jackal!
And the longer you tickle,
The louder he'll giggle
And jiggle
And joggle
And cackle
And wiggle.
And all through the jungle
They'll know that the jackal
Has heard a good jokel
Or had a good tickle.

journal

a notebook that you
write in every day

Opal's mother and father died when she was five years old, so Opal went to live with another family. She began to write a journal when she was six. She wrote about her new family. She wrote about the things she loved: the trees around her house and the mouse that lived under the front porch. And she wrote about her best friend, who was blind.

But when Opal was twelve, her journal was torn up. She saved all the pieces. Years later, she pasted the pieces back together like a puzzle.

Opal's Story

My mother and father are gone. . .
It is lonesome without them.
I like this house we live in
at the edge of the near woods
in the beautiful mountains.
Under the steps lives a toad.
I call him Virgil.
Under the house live some mice.
They have such beautiful eyes.
I give them bread to eat.

Today is taking egg day.
I put my blue bonnet on
and take eggs to the folks all around.
I put Felix the mouse in my pocket.
He does like to go for walks.
And sometimes he sleeps in my sleeve.
When he has wakeups,
we try to find cheese.
He has likes for cheese.

One way the road goes
to the house of the girl who
has no seeing.
When it gets to her house,
it makes a bend,
and it goes its way to the blue hills.
I tell her about the trees talking.
I tell her cloud ships are sailing
over the hills in a hurry.

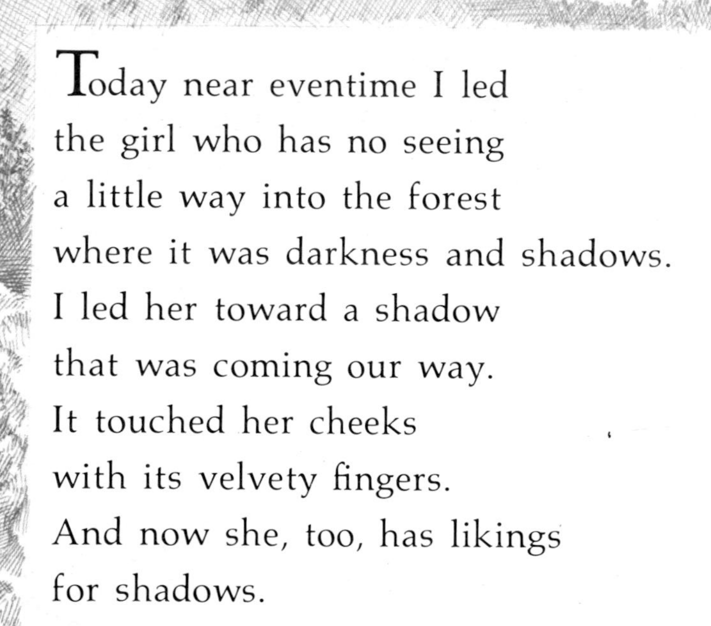

Today near eventime I led
the girl who has no seeing
a little way into the forest
where it was darkness and shadows.
I led her toward a shadow
that was coming our way.
It touched her cheeks
with its velvety fingers.
And now she, too, has likings
for shadows.

One of my tooths is loose and
has a queer feel.
The man who wears gray neckties
and is kind to mice
says tie a string around it
on a doorknob.
I did as he said.
I started to walk off.
Then I came back a ways.
I decided to wait a little while.
I walked off again.
Then I took the string off my tooth
and thought I'd wait till after dinner.

When I feel sad inside,
I talk things over with my tree.
I call him Michael Raphael.
When I go off the barn roof,
it is a long jump into his arms.
I might get my leg or neck broken.
So I always jump in a careful way.
It is such a comfort
to nestle up to Michael Raphael.

Some day I will write
about the big tree that I love.
Today I watch and did hear its moans
as the saw went through it.
There was a queer feel in my throat
and I couldn't stand up.
When the saw did stop,
there was a stillness.
There was a queer sad sound.
The big tree did quiver.
It did sway.
It did crash to the earth.
Oh, Michael Raphael!

Opal Whiteley

joy

wonderful happiness

The Kayak Paddler's Joy at the Weather

When I'm out of the house in the open,
I feel joy.
When I get out on the sea by chance,
I feel joy.
If it is really fine weather,
I feel joy.
If the sky really clears nicely,
I feel joy.

May it continue thus
for the good of my sealing!
May it continue thus
for the good of my hunting!
May it continue thus
for the good of my singing match!
May it continue thus
for the good of my drum song!

Richard Lewis

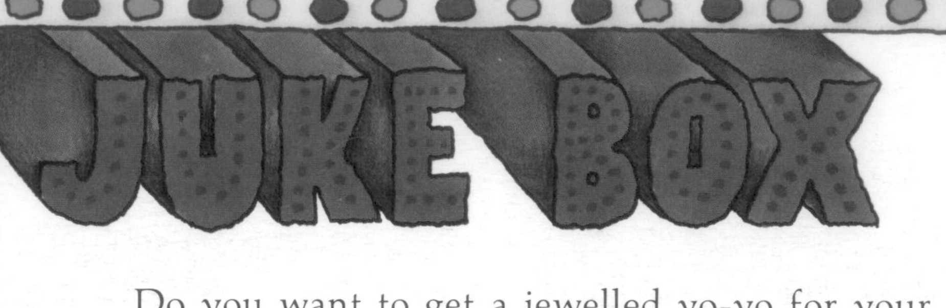

Do you want to get a jewelled yo-yo for your buddy's birthday—but you can't?

Do you want to send away for the Double Whammo—but you can't?

Do you want to get a new bell for your bike—but you can't?

Do you want to get the Fantastic-Plastic Wheel for your hamster—but you can't?

Well, if your piggy bank is empty and you are looking for a pocket-jingling way to make money, try the idea on the next page.

THE HUMAN
JUKE BOX
long song—5¢
short song—1¢
riddle without answer—1¢
riddle with answer—5¢
dumb joke—1¢
funny joke—5¢
loud yell—10¢
all of the above
plus hiccups—25¢

Kaleidoscope

Twist a magic tube of mirrors.
See colors and images
Dance and collide.
Multiplied,
A single sunbeam
Becomes a burst of stars.
A single flower
Becomes a chain of daisies.
And just one little girl
Becomes a circle of friends.
Twist a magic tube of mirrors.
See colors and images
Dance and collide.

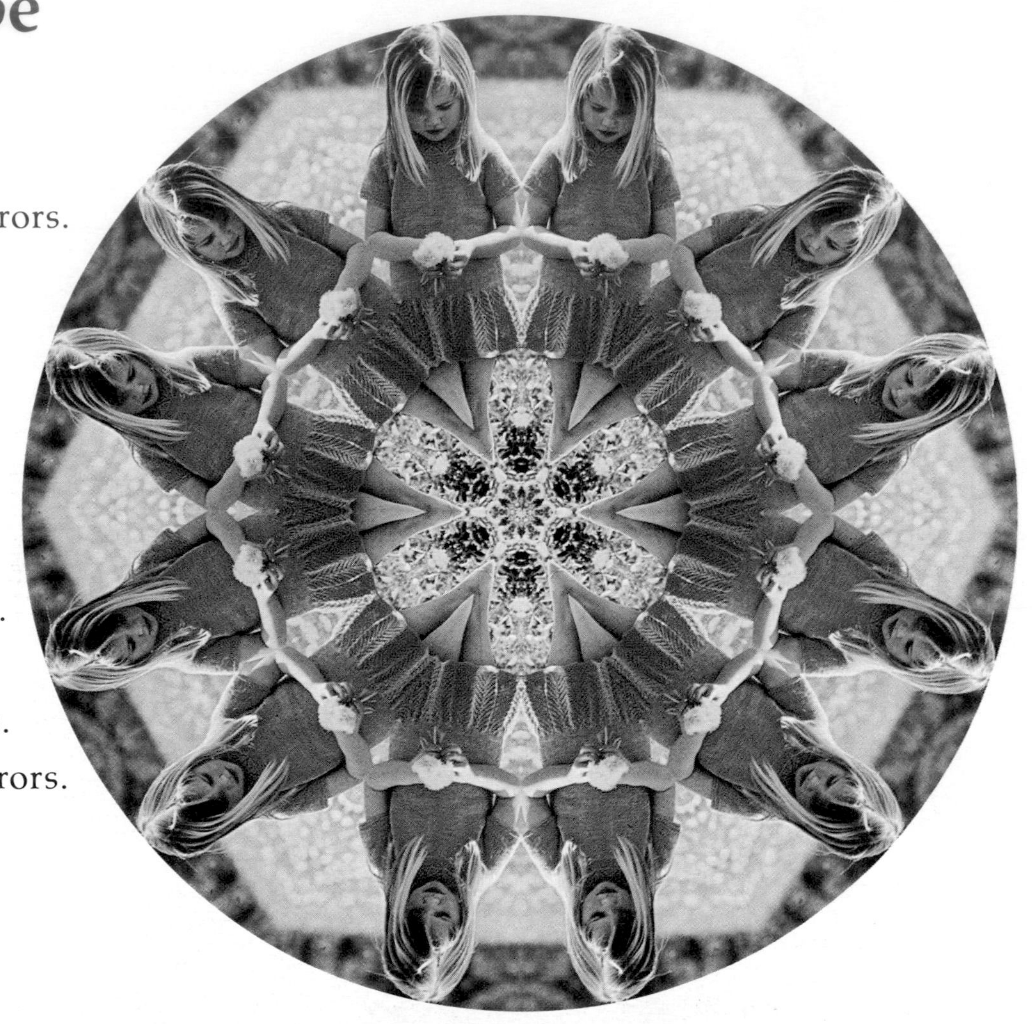

kangaroo

Australia
Monday, January 12

Hello, my little Kiddos,

Question: What looks like a kangaroo, leaps like a kangaroo, and wears a gold crown?

Answer: a kingaroo, of course!

In this country, kangaroos seem to be everywhere. They travel about in mobs (that's what you call a herd of kangaroos). Look at this snapshot of me with a mob of kangaroos. As you can see, they are very speedy fellows.

The male kangaroo is called a boomer, and the female is called a flyer--such funny names! But don't laugh. Kangaroos are strong. They can even leap over a moving car.

The very first thing a newborn kangaroo has to do is find its way into its mother's pouch. The baby kangaroo is called a joey. Once the joey is in the pouch, it stays there for many months, safe and warm. The joey sleeps. It drinks its mother's milk. It goes bouncing along wherever Mother goes. What a nice life!

Ta ta,

Uncle Rock

P.S. Here is a picture of a joey enjoying a free ride. Quite a life, don't you think?

karate

exercises that help you protect yourself

A person who teaches karate is called a *sensei,* which means "honorable teacher." A karate school is called a *dojo.* A karate uniform is called a *gi.*

Rico's First Spring

"It's cold. It's always cold in this city," Rico thought. "There are never warm breezes and sunny skies like there are back home. Some place this is—dirty streets, gray sky. Gray and cold, like the people. Gray and cold and mean."

Rico and his family had been in the city only a week. He hated it. Two days ago a gang of boys pushed his little sister, Teresita, into the snow. They took her wagon, her only toy. Teresita came running up the stairs crying, "Mama! Mama!" Rico rushed down the stairs and out into the street. But by the time he got outside, the boys had gone. Today, Teresita had found her wagon near the garbage cans. The wheels were gone, and the handle was bent and twisted.

Rico still felt angry inside. He had never felt like this before. It was an awful, ugly feeling. But he couldn't stop it. Each day on his way to school, he would think, "Maybe the sun will shine today. Maybe I'll make a friend in school today."

But when Rico reached the schoolyard, the other kids yelled at him and called him names. Rico was hurt and angry. He kicked an empty bottle against the old brick wall. The bottle broke into a thousand pieces.

Things only got worse. Teresita got sick and cried a lot. It seemed to rain every day. His mother's purse was stolen. When Rico heard that, he yelled, "I bet it was that gang. I hate all those guys. I hate this place. I hate everything here. I want to go home."

"Rico!" said his mother. "How dare you talk that way? I would rather lose every penny I have than hear my son say such things. What has happened to the good, quiet boy I had? Look at you. You act tough now. You speak tough. You are becoming just like the others."

Rico had never been so unhappy. He ran out of the apartment. The door slammed behind him. He went out into the street. He walked and walked. He didn't know where he was going. Before long, he was at 125th Street.

Suddenly he stopped. Some big trophies in a window caught his eye. There was a picture of a man wearing baggy pants and a shirt, with a wide

black belt around his waist. Rico looked up. The sign on the window said *Karate Studio*.

"Man!" thought Rico. "If I knew karate, no one would mess with me! I could really take care of myself and never get beat up."

There were some blue curtains pulled across the window. Rico peeked through. He could just see the man whose picture was in the window. The man moved in slow motion, kicking and punching the air. Rico stared, amazed.

"He's good, isn't he?" a voice said behind him. It was his father. He had been worried about Rico and had gone out to look for him. "Would you like to learn karate, Rico?"

"Oh, yes!" Rico said. It was the first time his voice had sounded happy in so long that he surprised himself.

"Oh, yes!" he said. "But it might cost a lot of money."

"Maybe we can work something out," his father said.

Rico and his father went inside. A half-hour later, Rico had a part-time job, cleaning up the studio after school. Instead of being paid, he would get free karate lessons.

After Rico's first day at the karate school, he ran excitedly into the apartment.

"Mama! It's just wonderful! My *sensei,* that's what you call a karate teacher, said I did very well. But it was really hard cleaning up the *dojo.*"

"The what?" Rico's mother asked.

"The *dojo*. That's the name for a karate school. Anyway, it was really hard sweeping after my lesson. My arms were so sore, I almost dropped the broom. Hey, do you want to see what I learned?"

Rico didn't wait for an answer. He started kicking and punching the air. "These are my karate exercises. I have to practice them every day."

Rico's mother was so glad to see him happy that she made him a special present. When Rico opened the box, there was a karate uniform made out of old sheets.

"Oh, Mama!" Rico said. "My very own *gi*!"

Karate was all that Rico could think about. As he swept the *dojo*, he watched the *sensei* work with the other students. The exercises they did were much too hard for a beginner.

"But someday, if I practice hard, I'll be able to do those exercises, too," Rico said to himself.

One day after karate class, Rico asked the *sensei*, "What are those markings on the wall?"

"That's Japanese writing. It means **respect**," said the *sensei*.

"Why did you write **respect** on the wall? Why didn't you write **fight**?" Rico asked.

"Because without respect, you'll never learn karate," said the *sensei*. "You have learned some of the karate exercises. You know how to kick, to duck, and to punch. But unless you are proud of your mind and body, you'll never really learn karate. Karate isn't just a way to fight. It's a new way to feel about yourself. It teaches you to have pride in yourself, right here inside. Remember, Rico. Respect. Pride. That's the real secret."

As Rico walked home, he thought about what his *sensei* had said. "Respect. Pride." He was not sure he understood. But he knew the *sensei* was serious.

Sunday was warmer than it had been. Spring was coming; not yet, but soon. The snow was melting. The air smelled a little greener, although no leaves were on the trees.

It was so nice outside that Rico decided to practice his karate exercises in the park. He could do exercises now that he had never dreamed of when he first stepped into the *dojo*. Rico walked onto the field. No one was around. He took off his jacket and shoes.

"Respect," he said to himself. "Respect." He felt pride in his feet and legs. Respect. He felt pride in his stomach and chest. Respect. He felt pride in his arms and hands. He felt respect for himself, for Rico Fontanez, standing there in the sunshine.

Very slowly, Rico began to move from one exercise to the next. He practiced each step carefully. He moved like a dancer. When Rico finished, he stood still for a minute, tall, straight, and filled with pride.

Then Rico noticed some boys looking at him. He recognized them at once. They were the ones who had smashed his sister's wagon. Maybe they were the ones who had taken his mother's purse, too.

"Hey, kid. What do you think you're doing?" asked the biggest guy.

Rico was surprised to find that he wasn't afraid at all. "Karate," he said, looking straight at the boys.

Nobody moved for a minute. Then the biggest guy said, "Did you learn that around here?"

Before Rico could answer, another boy broke in, "Can you teach me to kick like that? Wee-ooo, that's cool. Show me how you do it."

Rico was surrounded by the group of boys. He showed them some of the karate exercises. He tried not to laugh when they fell down. He remembered how he had felt the first day he had tried.

Suddenly, Rico understood what the *sensei* had meant about respect. Now that he respected himself, others respected him. All at once Rico felt a joyful pride inside. And he laughed and laughed.

Wendy Kesselman
and Norma Holt

New Zealand
Monday, January 19

Hi ho there, little Kiddos,

I flew over to visit some friends in New Zealand. Look at this picture of me-a with a kea.

And here is a poem about a kea, written for you-a by me-a.

I invited a kea to tea-a.
It was not how I thought
it would be-a.
I passed her the bread,
But the bird shook her head.
And here's what she said to me-a:

"I'd much prefer nectar,

Or buds from a tree-a.

But beetles and grubs

Are my favorites," said she-a.

I had none of those things--

Not a bug, not a flea-a.

It was very upsetting, I'm sure

you'll agree-a.

So I'll never again ask a kea

to tea-a.

Jolly good, don't you think?

Uncle Rock

P.S. Did you notice that

I have grown some fine

whiskers? A jolly good idea!

kerchoo

the sound a sneeze makes

MONDAY

Sneeze on Monday, sneeze for danger.

TUESDAY

Sneeze on Tuesday, kiss a stranger.

WEDNESDAY

Sneeze on Wednesday, get a letter.

THURSDAY

Sneeze on Thursday, get something better.

FRIDAY

Sneeze on Friday, sneeze for trouble.

SATURDAY

Sneeze on Saturday, fun is double.

SUNDAY

Sneeze on Sunday, too bad, too bad,
You sneeze away any luck you had.

Sky Seasoning

A piece of sky
Broke off and fell
Through the crack in the ceiling
Right into my soup,
KERPLOP!
I really must state
That I usually hate
Lentil soup, but I ate
Every drop!
Delicious delicious
(A bit like plaster),
But so delicious, goodness sake—
I could have eaten a lentil-soup lake.
It's amazing the difference
A bit of sky can make.

Shel Silverstein

key

Key has many meanings—

1. what you use to lock and unlock something
2. clue
3. symbols on a map

Mayor Knucklebuckle Leaves a Key

Mayor Knucklebuckle was missing. His house was empty. The phone was disconnected. There was nothing in the refrigerator but a jar of relish and a wrinkled lemon.

"Something is terribly wrong," said his secretary. "This is a case for La Snoupée, the Great Detective."

Ten minutes later La Snoupée, the Great Detective, was on the case.

The secretary wrung his hands. He wiped his forehead and told the detective all he knew.

"I know nothing," he said. "As you see, the house is empty. The refrigerator is empty, and Mayor Knucklebuckle is missing."

La Snoupée, the Great Detective, opened the refrigerator. "But yes!" she said. "We have two clues: a jar of relish and a wrinkled lemon."

The secretary began to relax.

"What a great detective you are. What do the clues mean?"

"Elementary," said the Great Detective. "Mayor Knucklebuckle likes relish on his hamburger and lemon on his fish."

"But where is the mayor?" asked the secretary.

"Perhaps he has gone to the supermarket," said the detective. "His food supply is rather low. Wait just a minute. What's this?" On top of the refrigerator was a map of the town. In the margin of the map was a message written in green ink.

⊙ You will find me here.

"This is a very important clue," said the Great Detective. "Look."

"What does it mean?" asked the secretary.

"Elementary," said the detective. "Mayor Knucklebuckle writes with green ink because he has run out of blue. He writes on the map because he has run out of paper. And he writes in the margin of the map because he has run out of town."

"But where?" asked the secretary.

"He doesn't say," answered the detective. "This is a most difficult case. I shall ask Chief Inspector Gotcha of the Police Department to assist me."

Eight minutes later Chief Inspector Gotcha arrived. His whole police force arrived with him. "Search this place completely," he said. "Tear down the walls. Rip up the floors. Take off the roof if you have to. But don't touch anything important."

Then the chief inspector joined the secretary and the detective in the kitchen. He inspected the refrigerator and the map. He nodded his head and said, "Ah yes, it is all very clear."

The secretary smiled brightly and straightened his tie. He was feeling very hopeful. "What does it all mean?" he asked.

"It is very clear," said the inspector. "The message is written in the margin of the map. Now, everyone knows that the margin of a map is nowhere at all. Therefore, the mayor has gone nowhere. Mayor Knucklebuckle is not missing."

"But—but—" said the secretary. "If the mayor is not missing, where is he now?"

"I am not sure," answered Inspector Gotcha. "Let me think."

Luckily for the chief inspector, a young girl walked in the door right then.

"Hello," she said. "Is Mayor Knucklebuckle having a party?"

"Who are you?" asked La Snoupée.

"What do you want?" asked Inspector Gotcha.

"Little girl," said the secretary, "the mayor is missing, and we haven't a clue to where he is."

"Correction," said La Snoupée, the Great Detective. "We have four clues."

"But they don't mean anything," said Inspector Gotcha. "If we could just find the key that will unlock the puzzle."

The little girl picked up the map and read the message.

"Why, you have the key," she said. "The mayor left a key right here in this message."

Nobody said anything. They just looked at the girl and waited.

The girl shook her head. "O.K., follow me! I'll show you where Mayor Knucklebuckle is."

And she did.

If you are not sure where Mayor Knucklebuckle is, turn to page 334.

kid

kin

Your kin are your relatives, the members of your family.

A chart of your kin is a picture of your family.

What does *your* kin chart look like?

kiwi

New Zealand
Monday, January 26

Dear little Kiddos,

There is something about the kiwi that reminds me of your very own Uncle Rock Bottomly.

Please note:

The kiwi is stout with short legs.
Sadly, so am I.

The kiwi has beady eyes.
So do I. (Some say I have sharp eyes, but others say they are just beady.)

The kiwi has long bristles at the base of its bill.
I believe I have already mentioned my whiskers.

The kiwi can't fly.

Neither can I.

The kiwi has no tail.

Neither do I.

Of course there are some differences. The kiwi has a big mouth and a loud, harsh voice. My mouth is medium small and rather nice, I think. I have been told my voice is very pleasant. Ah, well, thank goodness I have something to boast about. Poor kiwi doesn't seem to!

Toodle-oo!

Uncle Rock Bottomly

P.S. I just remembered one last point. I have no feathers! Ha, ha!

knight

a name for a soldier long ago

Knock-kneed knights knitted nifty knee socks nearly every night.

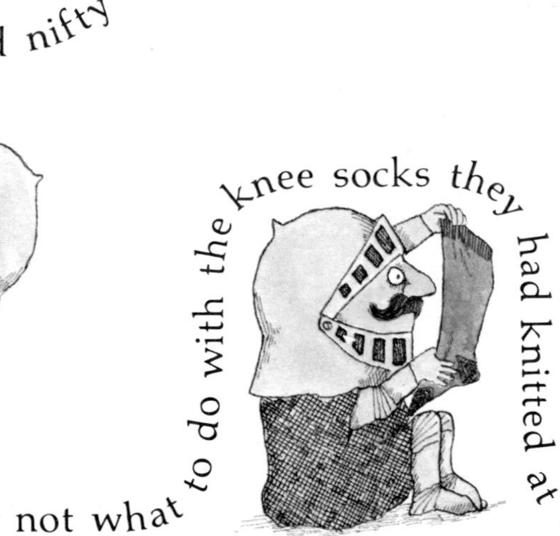

Knock-kneed knights knew not what to do with the knee socks they had knitted at night.

koala

Sydney, Australia
Monday, February 2

Hello! Hi ho! and all of that,

Here I am back in Australia, and here's a riddle for you:

I'm cuddly, furry, and squat.
I don't have a stripe or a spot.
I can hang by a claw.
I sound like a saw.
I look like a bear, but I'm not.

What am I?

a. bangaroo
b. koolewong
c. narnagoon
d. buidelbeer
e. karbor
f. cullawine
g. colo
h. New Holland sloth
i. koala
j. all of the above

The answer is j. All of these are names for a koala. Amazing, don't you think?

Cheerio,

Uncle Rock Bottomly

P.S. I'm sending you a picture of me with three cuddly koalas. I'm not so sure they wanted me in their tree. My photographer is getting better. Don't you agree?

labels

Laundry Soap
Clean Clean Clean!
Whiter whites and brighter brights!
More suds, cleaner duds!

Feb 82 LAR 50 LO
LEWIS LARDNER
50 LOCUST LANE
LANSING, LOUISIANA 00031

100% lambswool—made in England
Wash lukewarm 40 C.

GREEN LIMA BEANS

INGREDIENTS: LIMA BEANS, WATER, SALT, TRACE OF CALCIUM SALT ADDED.
NUTRITION INFORMATION PER ONE-CUP SERVING
(SERVINGS PER CONTAINER ABOUT 2)
CALORIES 150 CARBOHYDRATE 29G
PROTEIN 9G FAT 1G
Net wt. 17 oz. (1 lb. 1 oz.) or 482 grams

Luggage Printed in USA
LOFTY AIRLINES
FINAL DESTINATION Liverpool
PIECES 3 FLIGHT 137
LA 35-13-40

lap

Lap has many meanings.

The cat heard the water lap against the sides of the bowl.

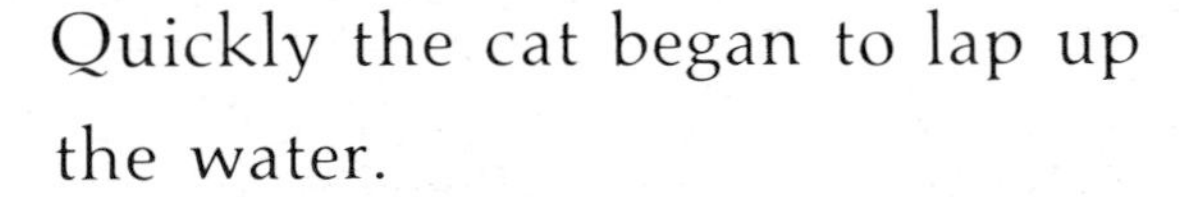

Quickly the cat began to lap up the water.

The goldfish was swimming a lap when it saw the cat.

Out jumped the goldfish—right into Sara's lap.

lava

There are two kinds of lava. Both kinds come from volcanoes.

A volcano is a cone-shaped mountain with an opening at the top. When a volcano erupts, there is a great explosion. Then ashes, steam, gases, and hot melted rock are forced out through the opening. The hot melted rock that pours from the volcano is called fire lava. When the fire lava cools, it hardens to stone.

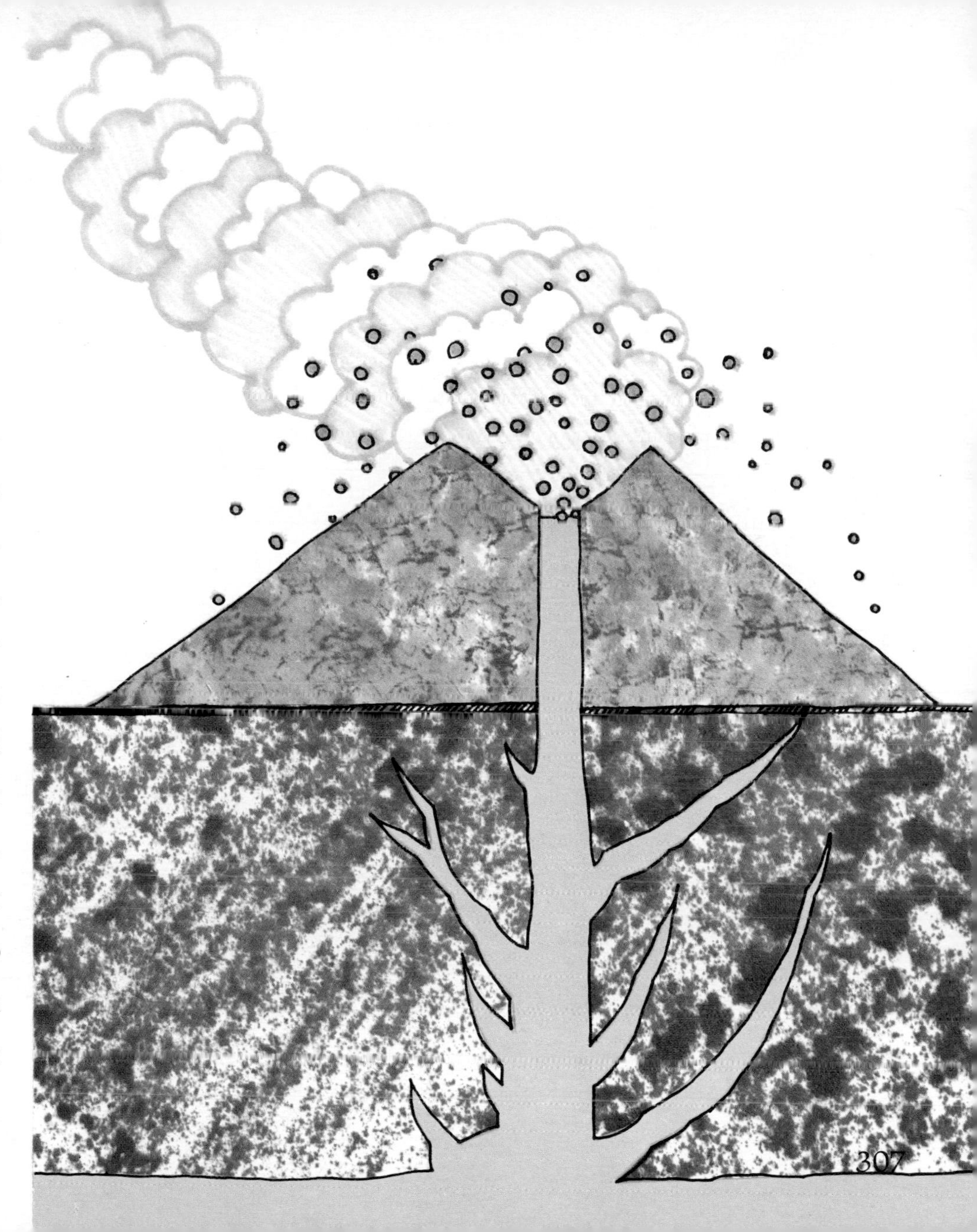

Mud lava is different. It is made of hot ashes from a volcano mixed with steam or water. Mud lava flows down the mountain like a thick river, covering everything in its path. Then it hardens.

Sometimes a volcano will not erupt for many years. Cities and towns are built on the hardened lava around it. On a hot August day in the year 79, a city in Italy called Herculaneum was buried by mud lava when nearby Mount Vesuvius exploded.

There is only one eyewitness report of this explosion. Seventeen-year-old Pliny wrote to a man called Tacitus to tell him what happened in Herculaneum on that August day nearly two thousand years ago.

My Dear Tacitus,

You asked me for a report on what happened the day that Mount Vesuvius exploded. I will tell you the unhappy story as best I can.

It was a hot August day. Uncle had finished lunch and was reading when Mother told him about the strange cloud that people had seen. He took his sandals and climbed a hill to look across the bay. Rising from Mount Vesuvius was a huge cloud. It was shaped like an umbrella tree and seemed to rise and fall. Sometimes it looked black; sometimes, white.

Uncle decided to sail across the bay to study the cloud more closely. Just as he was leaving, he heard that the mountain had exploded! People in Herculaneum needed help. So he told

people to get some bigger boats ready. They all set sail that afternoon.

Soon after he left, the earthquakes began. Our house bounced and swayed. Jars and vases broke. The walls began to crack. Mother and I decided to leave. The house was not safe. At any time, the walls might collapse.

Outside, thousands of people were running and screaming in the streets. Everybody was frightened. A strong wind had come up, and the cloud from Mount Vesuvius was blowing toward us.

Because the streets were so crowded, we headed toward the open fields. Just as we got there, the cloud covered us. It was so dark that Mother and I had to hold on to each other. It was like being in a room without windows or lights. I could not see my own hand. The air smelled terrible. I could not stop coughing.

Ashes fell faster than we could shake them off. All around us I could hear crying children and shouting men and women. The ashes covered our hair and clothes. Higher and higher they piled. We thought we were going to be buried alive.

Then the wind started blowing again, and we could breathe. The cloud of ashes blew away. When the sun came out, we could not believe what we saw around us. Ashes had covered everything like a soft, deep snow.

We hurried home and found the house still standing. There were

more earthquakes all that night. We sat up and waited for Uncle. But he never came back.

The next morning a friend of Uncle's arrived. He told us what had happened on the other side of the bay. Mount Vesuvius had erupted. Ashes fell on Herculaneum as they did here. But there the ashes mixed with water and made a river of mud. It flooded Herculaneum and completely buried the whole city.

I asked about Uncle. He had helped people reach the boats before lava covered the town. But he did not escape in time. They found his body near the boats of Herculaneum.

Pliny

This is a picture of the city Herculaneum today. The mud lava that buried Herculaneum hardened to stone. It kept the city the way it was the day the volcano erupted. Today, scientists called archaeologists have uncovered parts of Herculaneum. By digging away the mud lava, they have learned about the people who lived and worked in the houses and shops of Herculaneum.

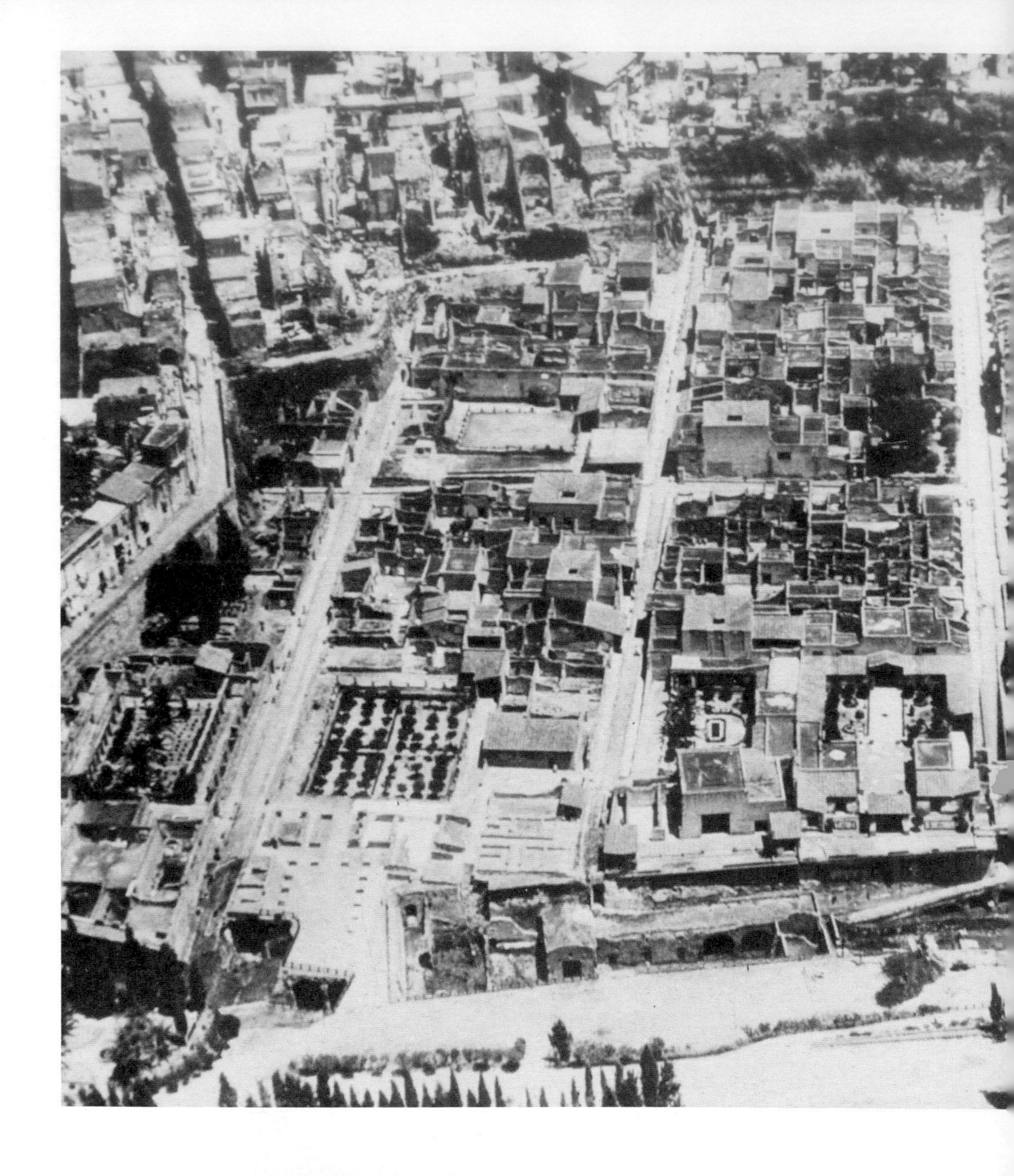

The grocery store was buried by mud lava. Archaeologists dug the mud away and then put all the bowls back where they found them. The glass case protects the bowls from being broken. The big jug in the front is still full of grain.

This was a bakery. Different kinds of cake pans hang on the wall in the back room. On the right are mills for grinding grain.

The garden of this house looks the way it did on the day Mount Vesuvius erupted. Pliny and his mother and his uncle lived in a house with a garden that looked like this one.

These old walnuts were found in a snack bar. They were preserved perfectly by the mud lava which flooded the city of Herculaneum.

The lamp stand was brought to this shop to be fixed. Two metal bars were ready to be used for repairs.

Archaeologists can't be certain at first what is buried in the mud lava. The mud lava buried this statue and then hardened. The hardened mud had to be chipped away very carefully.

leg

Here's a trick that's sure to fool all your buddies. Say, "I bet I can go out of the room on two legs and come back with six."

Someone is sure to want to see THAT!

What you do is just go pick up a chair in another room and bring it back with you.

The chair has four legs, and you have two; so you come back into the room with six legs!

legible

clear, neat writing

I can't stand

rotten writing

when it's written rotten.

leotard

Jules Leotard was an acrobat who lived more than one hundred years ago. He was the first man to use the flying-trapeze act in the circus. He also invented a costume for circus acrobats. The same kind of costume is worn by acrobats and dancers today. It is called a leotard.

Photograph © 1976 by Jill Krementz

lollygag

Do-nothings, dilly-dallyers, idlebacks, lazybones, poke-easies, and slugabeds love to lollygag.

A long time ago, the country store was a good place to lollygag. If you were lucky, you might be sent to the store on an errand. Your father might need some nails for the barn. Your sister might need some buttons for her dress. Your brother might need some medicine or liniment for the crick in his neck. Your grandmother might need some flour for bread. And after you'd done the errand, you could always lollygag at the store a little longer. You might look at the penny-candy jars. You might play a game of checkers on the cracker barrel. Or you might just sit by the pot-bellied stove and listen to the old-timers talk of days long ago.

I USE A LOT OF LEMON LINIMENT.
WHAT'S LEMON LINIMENT LIKE?
A LITTLE LEMON LINIMENT, PLEASE.
YUK! I HATE LEMON LINIMENT!

longer

the opposite of shorter

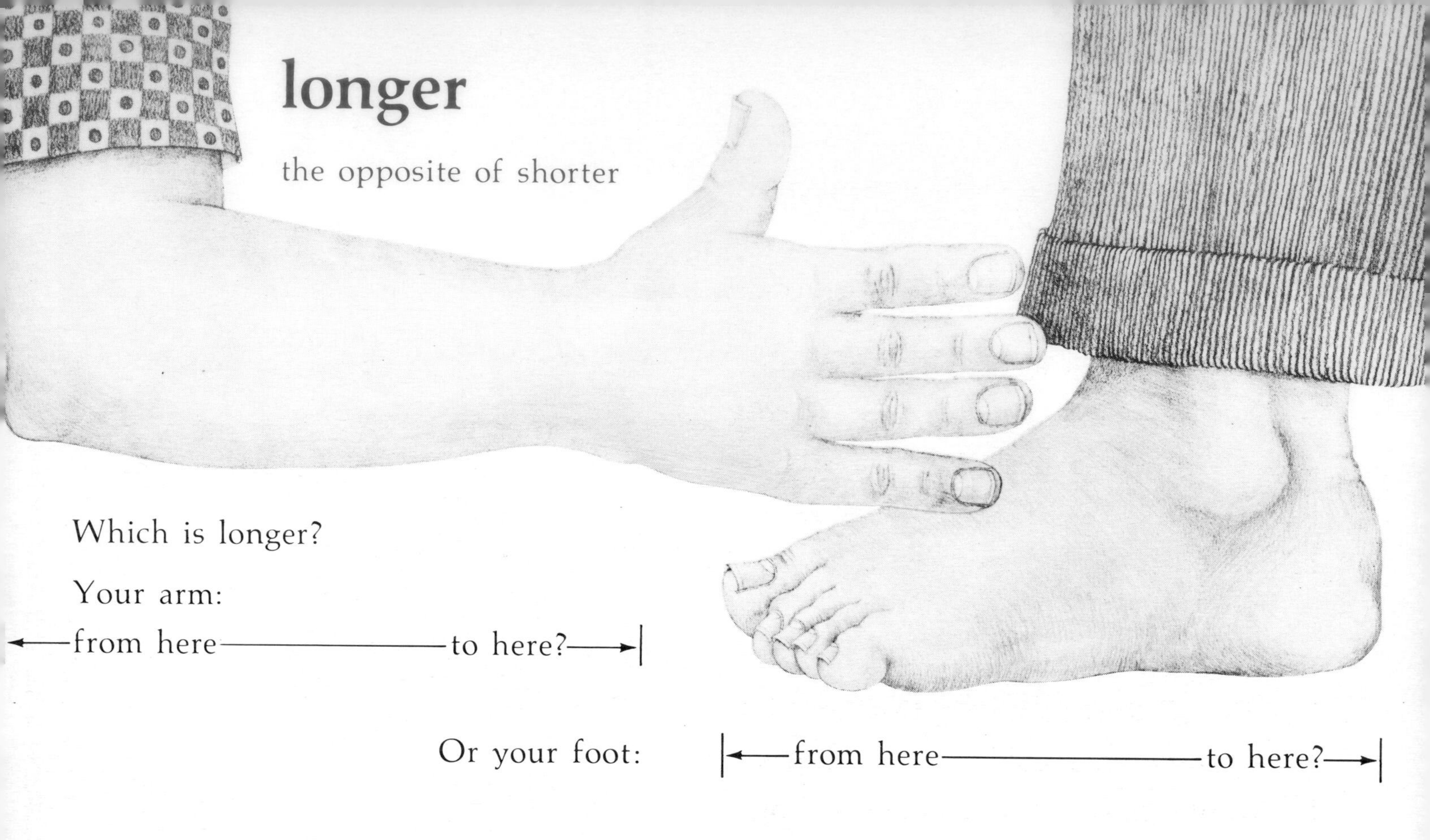

Which is longer?

Your arm:

←from here———————to here?→|

Or your foot: |←from here———————to here?→|

They are both about
the same length.
Prove it!
Measure them and see.

loom

a machine on which cloth is woven

The Crane Maiden

Many years ago, at the edge of a small mountain village, there lived an old man and his wife. They had little in this world, but they were happy in their life together.

One winter morning, the old man set out for the village. A bundle of firewood was tied to his back. It was so cold that he knew he would have little trouble selling the wood. With the money, he would buy some food for himself and his wife.

The old man was trudging through the falling snow when he

heard an unhappy cry. "Koh! Koh!"

The man went toward the sound, and he came upon a great crane caught in a trap. She was trying hard to free herself. The old man felt sorry for the beautiful bird. He talked to her quietly as he opened the trap. At once the crane flew into the air. Joyfully calling "Koh! Koh!" she disappeared into the snowy sky.

When the old man returned home, he told his wife about the crane.

"That was a good deed," she said. "One day you will be rewarded for your kind heart."

As she spoke, there came a tapping on the door. The woman hurried to open it. There stood a beautiful young girl. Her face glowed like a peach beginning to ripen in the summer sun. Her dark eyes sparkled in the dancing firelight.

"Forgive my knocking at your door," she said in a soft voice. "But I have lost my way in the snow." Then bowing low, she said, "My name is Tsuru-san."

"Oh, you poor child!" cried the old woman. "Come in at once before you freeze." She sat the girl down close to the fire.

The couple shared their simple supper of hot porridge with Tsuru-san. Then they gave her their bed with its warm quilts to sleep on while they spent the night on a pile of straw.

In the morning when they awoke, the old man and woman were surprised to see a good fire already burning. The water bowl was filled with fresh, clear water. The floors had been swept.

Tsuru-san, the sleeves of her kimono neatly tied back with a red cord, was busily stirring a pot over the fire. "Good morning," she said, bowing to the old couple. "If you will wash your hands, we can eat breakfast. The porridge is cooked and ready."

"In our old age we have a fine daughter!" said the man, laughing.

"We are smiled upon because of your good deed yesterday," answered his wife happily.

The snow and bitter cold lasted for many days. Tsuru-san stayed in the old couple's home. Since she had no mother or father, in the end it was decided that she would live with them as their daughter.

The children of the neighborhood soon began coming to play with the new girl. The house that had been so still and quiet now rang with happy laughter. The hearts of the old man and his wife were filled with joy.

So the days of early winter passed. Soon it would be time for the great New Year celebration. The old man said to his wife, "Tsuru-san has been such a delight to us. If only we could give her a New Year's gift."

"Yes. But there is no money even for rice," his wife said.

Tsuru-san overheard them talking. It made her sad that these good people should be so poor. She came to them, bowed low, and said, "Dear parents, perhaps I can help you and repay your great kindness to me. There is an old loom in the back room. I will weave cloth on it for you to sell in the village. But you must promise that no one shall look at me while I am weaving."

The old man and his wife thought this was strange. But they agreed.

Tsuru-san locked herself in the back room. Soon the old couple heard her weaving. The sound of the loom was almost like a song:

"Tin kola, kola, pon, pon.
Tin kola, kola, pon, pon."

For three days Tsuru-san worked at the loom. At last the door opened. Tsuru-san stepped out. In her arms was the most beautiful cloth that the old man and his wife had ever seen.

"Dear parents," Tsuru-san said, "take this into the village and sell it. It will help a little to thank you for the happy home you have given me."

The old man hurried into the village. A crowd gathered around him when they saw the beautiful cloth. Each person offered more money than the last, and the cloth was finally sold for one hundred pieces of gold.

The old man bought rice for rice cakes and a kimono for Tsuru-san. Then he hurried home, singing.

The old man and his wife hustled and bustled. The old man pounded rice. The old woman made it into fine

white cakes. On New Year's Day, all the children came for a great party with their friend, Tsuru-san.

So time passed happily in the couple's home. One day Tsuru-san said, "It is time for me to weave more cloth, dear parents. You need money to live until the spring returns. But remember what I told you. No one is to look at me while I am working."

Again they promised. So the girl locked herself in the back room again and began to weave on the loom. Once more the loom sang,

"Tin kola, kola, pon, pon.
Tin kola, kola, pon, pon."

One day passed quickly and then another. By now the neighbors had grown curious.

"Is Tsuru-san weaving again?" asked one.

"Ah, soon you will have more gold pieces to hide under the floor," said another with a smile and a wink.

"How does Tsuru-san weave such cloth?" asked another neighbor.

"We do not know. We have promised not to watch her while she works," said the old man.

"How strange!" cried the neighbor. "I would not make such a promise to *my* daughter."

The old couple had been very curious about Tsuru-san's weaving. So the old man stepped up to a crack in the door.

"Stop, stop, old man!" cried his wife when she saw what was happening. "Tsuru-san has forbidden it!"

But it was too late. He had already peeked through the crack.

What a surprise! There, sitting at

the loom, was the great white crane he had rescued. She was pulling feathers from her body and magically weaving them into cloth.

The old man stepped back from the door. Before he could say what he had seen, the door opened. Out stepped Tsuru-san. Thin and pale, she held in her hands a half-finished piece of cloth.

"Dear parents," she said in a

weak voice, "yes, it is true. I am the crane you rescued from the trap. I wanted to repay your kindness." Then her eyes filled with tears. "But now that you have seen me in my true form, I can no longer stay with you."

With this, she kissed the old man and woman tenderly and walked out of the house. Instantly she became a crane once more. With a great swish of her wings, she flew up into the sky. Slowly she circled overhead. Then with a single sad cry, "Koh!" the crane maiden was gone forever.

Miyoko Matsutani

I would love you
If you were mine.

I would love you
If you weren't mine.

I still love you
Even though
You aren't mine.

Eleanor Schick

answer page

arithmetic

autograph

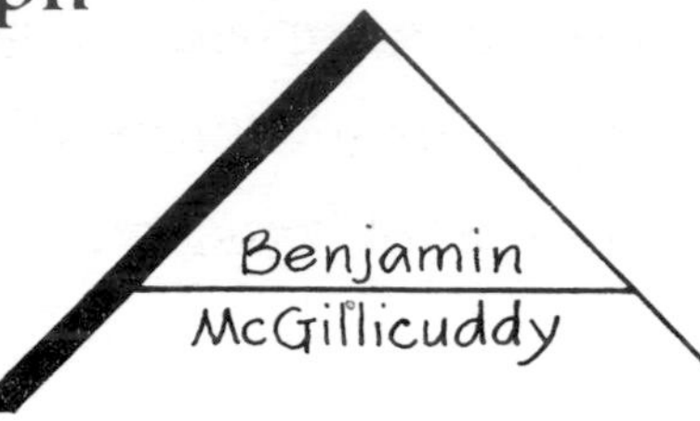

elevator

She couldn't reach the button for 12.

gear

The last gear turns this way.

glass

Take glass 4 and pour the water into glass 1. Then put glass 4 back.

head

No, because he had to wake up before he could ring the bell!

key

Glossary

This Glossary lists some of the words used in the Reader. The Glossary tells how to pronounce the words. It also gives one or more meanings for each word. The meanings are the ones used in the stories.

To help you pronounce the words, every word is respelled with the letters and signs of the Pronunciation Key below. The syllable that gets the heaviest accent is set in heavy type. This mark ′ follows it. This mark ′ follows a syllable that gets a lighter accent.

A short form of the Pronunciation Key appears at the bottom of each left-hand page of the Glossary.

Full Pronunciation Key

a	hat, cap	**i**	it, pin	**ou**	house, out	**w**	will, woman
ā	age, face	**ī**	ice, five	**p**	paper, cup	**y**	young, yet
ä	father, far	**j**	jam, enjoy	**r**	run, try	**z**	zero, breeze
b	bad, rob	**k**	kind, seek	**s**	say, yes	**zh**	measure, seizure
ch	child, much	**l**	land, coal	**sh**	she, rush		
d	did, red	**m**	me, am	**t**	tell, it		
e	let, best	**n**	no, in	**th**	thin, both	**ə**	represents:
ē	equal, be	**ng**	long, bring	**ŦH**	then, smooth		a in about
ėr	term, learn	**o**	hot, rock	**u**	cup, butter		e in taken
f	fat, if	**ō**	open, go	**u̇**	full, put		i in pencil
g	go, bag	**ô**	order, all	**ü**	rule, move		o in lemon
h	he, how	**oi**	oil, voice	**v**	very, save		u in circus

A

ache (**āk**) To be in pain; hurt.

ac•ro•bat (**ak′** rə bat) A person who can perform stunts, such as swinging on a trapeze, walking on a tightrope, and so on.

ad•vice (ad **vīs′**) An opinion about what should be done; suggestion.

ad•vise (ad **vīz′**) To give an opinion to.

Af•ri•can (**af′** rə kən) Of Africa or its people.

a•hoy (ə **hoi′**) A call used by sailors to get the attention of persons at a distance.

al•ley (**al′** ē) A narrow back street in a city or town.

all of the a•bove (**ôl əv ᴛʜə** ə **buv′**) Everything one sees written above.

an•ten•nae (an **ten′** ē) Long, thin feelers used for sensing by touch.

ap•pe•tite (**ap′** ə tīt) A desire for food.

ar•chae•ol•o•gist (är′ kē **ol′** ə jist) A person who studies old buildings, tools, pottery, and other objects in order to find out how people lived.

ar•ma•dil•lo (är′ mə **dil′** ō) A small, digging animal with a shell of bony plates that protects it.

Aus•tral•ia (ô **strā′** lyə) A continent southeast of Asia.

B

bal•lad (**bal′** əd) A poem that tells a story. Ballads are often sung.

bal•let (**bal′** ā) A story-telling dance done by a group on a stage.

bank (**bangk**) The ground along the sides of a river or lake; shore.

bare (**ber**) Without covering; not clothed.

base (**bās**) The bottom part; the part on which something stands.

a hat; **ā** age; **ä** father, far; **e** let; **ē** be; **ėr** term; **i** it; **ī** ice; **ng** long; **o** hot; **ō** open; **ô** order; **sh** she; **th** thin; **ᴛʜ** then; **u** cup; **u̇** full; **ü** rule; **zh** measure; **ə** represents **a** in about, **e** in taken, **i** in pencil, **o** in lemon, **u** in circus.

bay (bā) A part of a sea or lake extending into the land.

bit•ter (bit′ ər) Having a sharp, bad taste.

blush (blush) To become red in the face because of shame or confusion.

boast (bōst) To speak too highly of oneself or what one owns; brag.

bored (bôrd) Feeling tired because of dull talk or happenings.

bow (bou) The front part of a ship, boat, or airplane.

bris•tle (bris′ əl) One of the short, stiff hairs of some animals or plants.

broke (brōk) 1. Without money. 2. Cracked a bone.

bron•to•sau•rus (bron′ tə **sôr′** əs) A huge, plant-eating dinosaur.

buf•fa•lo (buf′ ə lō) A North American wild ox. It has a humped back, a shaggy coat, and a big head with short horns.

bump•er (bum′ pər) A bar across the front of a buggy or car that protects it from damage.

bur•i•al ground (ber′ ē əl **ground)** Land used for burying the dead. For some animals, it is a place where they go alone to die.

burst (bėrst) A sudden breaking out.

butt (but) To strike or push by knocking hard with the head. **butt in** To meddle or interfere.

C

C. Short for Celsius **(sel′** sē əs) A scale for measuring temperature.

cas•se•role (kas′ ə rōl′) Food that is cooked and served in a covered baking dish.

cast (kast) A case made of plaster that is used to hold a broken bone in place.

cat•tle (kat′ l) Cows, bulls, and steers that are raised for meat, milk, hides, and so on.

cell (**sel**) A small, hollow place.

charge (**chärj**) To attack; rush with force.

chem•i•cal (**kem′** ə kəl) Any substance made by or used in a chemical process.

chick•en pox (**chik′** ən **poks**) A mild disease of children in which spots appear on the skin.

chief in•spec•tor (**chēf** in **spek′** tər) A person in charge who looks at or examines things to get information.

chill (**chil**) To make or become cold.

clev•er (**klev′** ər) Smart; having a quick mind.

clum•sy (**klum′** zē) Not graceful in moving.

coin (**koin**) A piece of metal stamped by a government for use as money.

col•lapse (kə **laps′**) 1. To fall down in a heap. 2. To cave in.

col•lide (kə **līd′**) To strike each other; crash together.

com•fort (**kum′** fərt) A person or thing that makes life easier or takes away hardship.

con•tact (**kon′** takt) A touching together.

con•trap•tion (kən **trap′** shən) An object put together in an odd way.

cou•ple (**kup′** əl) A man and woman who are married, engaged, partners in a dance or other activity.

cow•punch•er (**kou′** pun′ chər) A person who drives cattle.

crack•er bar•rel (**krak′** ər **bar′** əl) A large wooden container with a round, flat top and bottom and sides that curve out slightly, used to hold crackers.

crease (**krēs**) A line made by folding cloth, paper, and so on; fold.

cre•a•tive (krē **ā′** tiv) Newly made from imagination; not copied.

crea•ture (**krē′** chər) Any living person or animal.

crum•my (**krum′** ē) No good; terrible.

D

dan•gle (**dang′** gəl) To hang and swing loosely.

a hat; ā age; ä father, far; e let; ē be; ėr term; i it; ī ice; ng long; o hot; ō open; ô order; sh she; th thin; ᴛʜ then; u cup; u̇ full; ü rule; zh measure; ə represents a in about, e in taken, i in pencil, o in lemon, u in circus.

deed (**dēd**) A thing done; act; action.

de•light (di **līt′**) Something that gives great pleasure.

de•scrip•tion (di **skrip′** shən) A telling in words how a person, place, thing, or event looks or behaves.

des•ert (**dez′** ərt) A dry area that is usually sandy and without trees.

di•no•saur (**dī′** nə sôr) Any of a large group of reptiles that lived millions of years ago.

dis•ap•pear (dis ə **pir′**) To pass from sight; stop being seen.

dis•con•nect•ed (dis′ kə **nek′** tid) No longer plugged in to a source of power; unfastened.

dis•ease (də **zēz′**) Sickness; illness.

di•ver (**dī′** vər) A person who dives under water.

do-dad•der (**dü′** dad ər) A person who does many different kinds of things.

door frame (**dôr′** frām′) A border in which a door is set.

drag•on•fly (**drag′** ən flī) A large, harmless insect with a long body and two pairs of light, thin wings.

draw•bridge (**drô′** brij′) A bridge that can be lifted and lowered. In old castles, drawbridges were lifted to keep people out.

E

earth•quake (**ėrth′** kwāk′) Shaking or sliding of a part of the earth's crust.

el•e•gant (**el′** ə gənt) Showing good taste; beautiful; luxurious.

el•e•men•tar•y (el′ ə **men′** tər ē) Simple; easy.

em•per•or (**em′** pər ər) A man who rules an empire.

er•rand (**er′** ənd) 1. A trip to do something. 2. A small job to be done.

e•rupt (i **rupt′**) To throw forth; to burst.

eu•re•ka (yu̇ **rē′** kə) I have found it! (Happy cry made at a discovery.)

e•ven•time (**ē′** vən tīm′) Evening.

ex•per•i•ment (ek **sper′** ə ment) To try in order to find out; make tests.

eye•wit•ness (**ī′** wit′ nes) A person who has actually seen something happen and can tell about it.

F

fac•tor•y (**fak′** tər ē) A place where things are made with machines or by hand.

fan•tas•tic (fan **tas′** tik) Great; unbelievably good.

fate (**fāt**) What becomes of a person or thing.

feel•er (**fē′** lər) A special part of an animal's body for sensing by touch.

fib (**fib**) To tell a lie about some small matter.

fidg•et (**fij′** it) To move about nervously; be uneasy.

fish hatch•er•y (**fish hach′** ər ē) A place for hatching fish eggs.

flak (**flak**) Criticism.

fla•min•go (flə **ming′** gō) A pink-and-scarlet wading bird with very long legs and neck.

fly•ing-tra•peze (**flī′** ing trə **pēz′**) A very high swing used to do tricks in the circus.

for•bid•den (fər **bid′** n) Not allowed; against the rules.

fur•i•ous (**fyu̇r′** ē əs) Full of wild anger.

G

G Short for gram (**gram**) A unit for measuring weight.

ga•lumph (gə **lumpf′**) To move with a clumsy, bumping, heavy-footed walk.

gear (**gir**) A wheel with teeth on the edge. The teeth fit together with the teeth of another gear. When one gear turns, it causes the next gear to turn.

goal (**gōl**) Something desired.

a hat; **ā** age; **ä** father, far; **e** let; **ē** be; **ėr** term; **i** it; **ī** ice; **ng** long; **o** hot; **ō** open; **ô** order; **sh** she; **th** thin; **ŧh** then; **u** cup; **u̇** full; **ü** rule; **zh** measure; **ə** represents **a** in about, **e** in taken, **i** in pencil, **o** in lemon, **u** in circus.

goose•bum•py (**güs′** bump′ ē) Having bumps on the skin, like those on a plucked goose, caused by fear or cold.

grasp (**grasp**) To hold something tightly by closing the fingers around it.

graze (**grāz**) To feed on growing grass.

grease (**grēs**) Soft, melted animal fat.

grub (**grub**) A soft, thick, wormlike form of an insect.

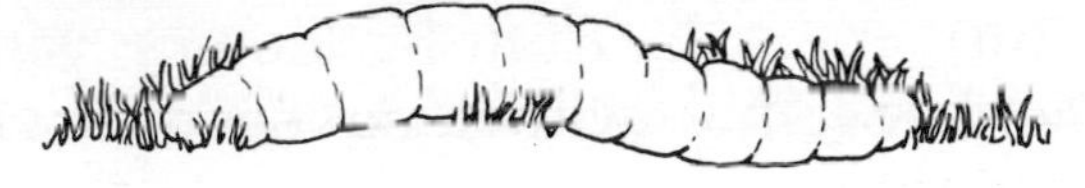

grum•ble (**grum′** bəl) To mutter; complain in an unhappy way.

gulp (**gulp**) To catch the breath by swallowing hard.

H

harm (**härm**) Something that causes pain or injury.

harsh (**härsh**) Sharp or unpleasant to touch, taste, see, or hear.

har•vest (**här′** vist) To gather in food crops and bring them home for use.

haunt•ed (**hôn′** tid) Visited by ghosts.

health•y (**hel′** thē) Free from sickness; well.

herd (**hėrd**) A group of animals of one kind that keep, feed, and move together.

herd•er (**hėr′** dər) A person who takes care of a group of animals, such as cows or sheep, and keeps them together.

hu•man (**hyü′** mən) Having or showing qualities natural to people.

I

im•age (**im′** ij) A likeness or copy.

i•mag•ine (i **maj′** ən) To picture in one's mind.

in•gre•di•ent (in **grē′** dē ənt) Any one of the parts of a mixture.

in•ner (**in′** ər) Farther in; inside.

in•sect (**in′** sekt) Any of a group of small animals with no backbone and with the body in three parts. Insects have three pairs of legs, and one or two pairs of wings. Flies, bees, beetles, butterflies, and grasshoppers are insects.

in•tro•duce (in′ trə **düs′**) To make known.

i•ron (**ī′** ərn) Made of a hard, strong silver-gray metal.

is•land (**ī′** lənd) A small body of land with water all around it.

J

jack•al (jak′ əl) A wild dog of Asia, Africa, and eastern Europe, as big as a fox. Jackals hunt in packs at night. They feed on small animals they catch and on animals they find dead.

Jap•a•nese (jap′ ə **nēz′**) Of Japan, its people, or their language.

jol•ly good (jol′ ē **gu̇d**) Very good; excellent.

judge (juj) To decide who wins a race, contest, and so on.

K

kay•ak (kī′ ak) An Eskimo canoe made of skins stretched over a light frame with an opening in the middle for a person.

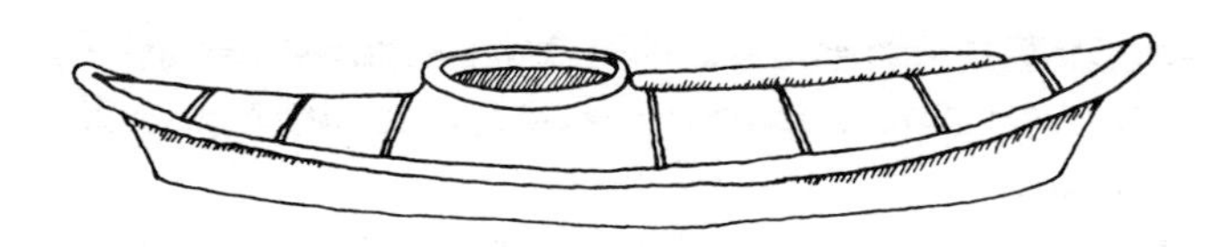

ker•choo (kėr **chū′**) A sound of a sneeze.

ki•mo•no (kə **mō′** nə) A loose robe or gown held in place by a sash. It is worn by Japanese men and women.

knit (nit) To make cloth by looping yarn or thread together with long needles or by machine.

knock-kneed (nok′ nēd′) Having legs bent inward at the knees.

L

length (lengkth) How long a thing is; what a thing measures from end to end.

len•til soup (len′ tl **süp**) A soup made from small, flat, beanlike seeds.

lick•e•ty-split (lik′ ə tē **split′**) At full speed.

life•boat (līf′ bōt′) A strong boat, usually carried on a large ship, used for saving lives at sea.

a hat; **ā** age; **ä** father, far; **e** let; **ē** be; **ėr** term; **i** it; **ī** ice; **ng** long; **o** hot; **ō** open; **ô** order; **sh** she; **th** thin; **ᴛʜ** then; **u** cup; **u̇** full; ü rule; **zh** measure; **ə** represents **a** in about, **e** in taken, **i** in pencil, **o** in lemon, **u** in circus.

life jacket (**līf jak′** it) A sleeveless jacket filled with a light material, like cork or air, worn to keep a person afloat in the water.

lin•go (**ling′** gō) Talk that sounds strange.

lin•i•ment (**lin′** ə mənt) A liquid rubbed on the skin to relieve the pain of sore muscles, sprains, and so on.

lone•some (**lōn′** səm) Feeling alone and sad.

lug•gage (**lug′** ij) Bags, boxes, or suitcases used to carry a traveler's belongings.

lux•ur•i•ous (lug **zhůr′** ē əs) Very comfortable and beautiful.

M

maid•en (**mād′** n) A young unmarried woman; girl.

mane (**mān**) Long, heavy hair growing on the back of or around the neck of an animal.

mar•gin (**mär′** jən) A blank space around the edge of a page.

mass (**mas**) A large amount of something lumped together.

match (**mach**) A game; contest.

may•or (**mā′** ər) A person at the head of a city or town government.

mess with (**mes with**) To bother; interfere with.

miles an hour (**mīls ən our**) A unit of measure for the number of miles that can be traveled in one hour.

mis•sion (**mish′** ən) A special job that a person or a group of people is sent to do.

moat (**mōt**) A deep, wide ditch dug around a castle long ago. Moats were usually filled with water to make it hard for people to get into the castle.

mole (**mōl**) A small animal that lives underground most of the time. Moles have fur like velvet and very small eyes that do not see well.

mon•ster (**mon′** stər) A creature from the imagination having a strange and horrible look.

Ms. (**miz**) A title put in front of a woman's name.

mul•ti•plied (**mul′** tə plīd) Increased in numbers.

mur•mur (**mėr′** mər) To say in a low voice.

mus•cle (**mus′** əl) A part of the body that can be tightened or loosened to make the body move. **make a muscle** To enlarge the upper-arm muscle in order to scare or impress someone.

N

nec•tar (**nek′** tər) A sweet liquid found in many flowers.

nerv•ous (**ner′** vəs) Jumpy; easily excited or upset.

nes•tle (**nes′** əl) To settle oneself comfortably or cozily.

net wt. Short for net weight (**net wāt**) The weight of what is inside a jar, box, and so on.

New Zea•land (**nü zē′** lənd) A country in the South Pacific. It has two main islands and some small ones.

nif•ty (**nif′** tē) Fine, attractive, or stylish.

night•fall (**nīt′** fôl′) The coming of night; dusk.

note (**nōt**) To pay attention to; take notice.

nude (**nüd**) Having no clothes on; naked.

O

old-tim•er (**old′ tī′** mər) A person who has lived in one place for a long time.

op•er•a (**op′** ər ə) A play in which music is an important part. In an opera, people sing alone or in groups. An orchestra plays with the singers.

o•rig•i•nal (ə **rij′** ə nəl) Not like any other; new.

oys•ter (**oi′** stər) A shellfish having an irregular shell in two halves. Oysters are found in shallow waters along seacoasts.

oz. Short for ounce (**ouns**) A unit for measuring weight.

a hat; **ā** age; **ä** father, far; **e** let; **ē** be; **ėr** term; **i** it; **ī** ice; **ng** long; **o** hot; **ō** open; **ô** order; **sh** she; **th** thin; **ᴛʜ** then; **u** cup; **u̇** full; **ü** rule; **zh** measure; **ə** represents **a** in about, **e** in taken, **i** in pencil, **o** in lemon, **u** in circus.

P

pas•sen•ger (**pas′** n jər) A person who travels in a car, airplane, bus, ship, train, and so on.

pas•sing (**pas′** ing) The act of getting a ball or other object to a teammate in a game.

patch•work quilt (**pach′** wėrk′ **kwilt**) A two-layered bed cover. It is made of pieces of cloth of many colors sewed together. For warmth, it has a lining or pad between the two outer layers.

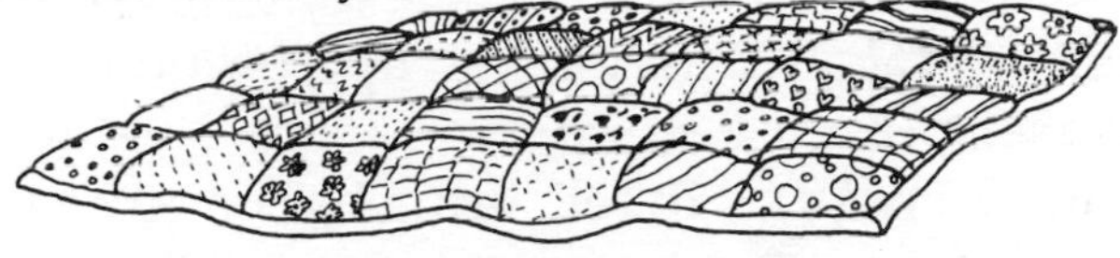

pearl (**pėrl**) A rounded, white or nearly white gem that is formed inside the shell of an oyster or other similar shellfish.

pe•cul•iar (pi **kyü′** lyər) Strange; odd.

pest (**pest**) A thing or person that causes trouble or harm.

pes•ter (**pes′** tər) To bother; trouble.

pick•led (**pik′** əld) Preserved in vinegar or salt water.

pi•rate (**pī′** rit) A person who attacks and robs ships.

plan•et (**plan′** it) A large heavenly body that moves in a circle around the sun. Mercury, Venus, Earth, and so on, are planets.

plas•ter (**plas′** tər) A covering for walls or ceilings. It is a soft mixture of lime, sand, and water that hardens as it dries.

plumb•er (**plum′** ər) A worker who puts in or fixes water pipes in buildings.

point (**point**) An important detail or idea.

pol•lu•ted (pə **lü′** ted) Dirty, especially from waste matter.

pol•lu•tion (pə **lü′** shən) Anything that dirties the air, water, or land, especially waste matter.

pot•bel•lied stove (**pot′** bel′ ēd **stōv**) A stove having the shape of a large, round belly in which wood or coal is burned for heat.

pouch (**pouch**) A baglike fold of skin. A kangaroo carries its young in a pouch.

pre•fer (pri **fėr′**) To like better.

pre•serve (pri **zėrv′**) To keep from change or harm.

prick•ly (**prik'** lē) Having many sharp points or thorns.

proud (**proud**) Feeling great joy from being honored.

prune (**prün**) A kind of sweet dried plum.

P.S. (**pē es**) Short for postscript; an addition to a letter, written after the writer's name has been signed.

Q

quiv•er (**kwiv'** ər) To shake; shiver; tremble.

R

ra•dar (**rā'** där) An instrument that sends out radio waves, which bounce back after they hit some object. Radar is used to find out the distance, direction, and speed of airplanes, ships, storms, and so on.

rare (**rer**) Seldom seen or found.

re•al•ize (**rē'** ə līz) To understand clearly; be fully aware of.

re•cord (**rek'** ərd) A thin piece of plastic on which sounds have been recorded to be played back.

re•cord•ing (ri **kôr'** ding) A tape or record that plays back a message.

rec•tan•gu•lar (rek **tang'** gyə lər) Shaped like a rectangle.

re•fuse (ri **fyüz'**) To say no to; say one will not do something.

re•lax (ri **laks'**) To loosen up; become less tense.

re•port (ri **pôrt'**) To tell; bring back a story of.

re•port•er (ri **pôr'** tər) A person who gathers news for a newspaper, magazine, radio or TV station, and so on.

re•spect (ri **spekt'**) 1. To feel or show honor for. 2. Honor; high regard.

re•ward (ri **wôrd'**) To give something for a service or task done.

rig•a•ma•role (**rig'** ə mə rōl') Foolish talk.

roar (**rôr**) 1. To rush with great speed and noise. 2. To make a loud, deep sound.

a hat; **ā** age; **ä** father, far; **e** let; **ē** be; **ėr** term; **i** it; **ī** ice; **ng** long; **o** hot; **ō** open; **ô** order; **sh** she; **th** thin; **ᴛʜ** then; **u** cup; **u̇** full; **ü** rule; **zh** measure; **ə** represents **a** in about, **e** in taken, **i** in pencil, **o** in lemon, **u** in circus.

robe (**rōb**) A blanket made of the skin of an animal.

roll (**rōl**) Something turned round and round on itself or on something else.

rude (**rüd**) Not polite.

ruf•fle (**ruf′** əl) A strip of cloth, ribbon, or lace pulled together along one edge and used for trimming.

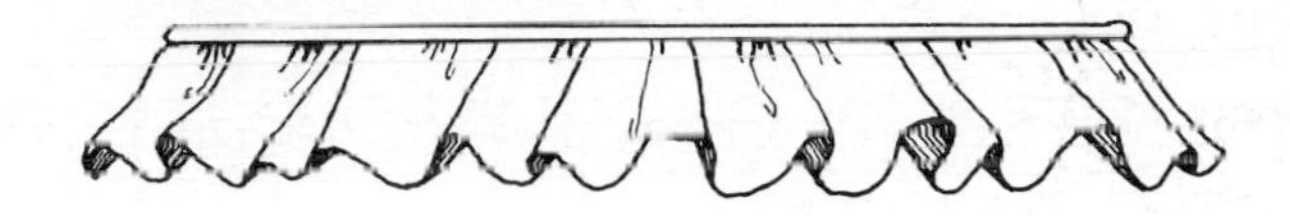

S

sa•la•mi (sə **lä′** mē) A kind of thick sausage, sometimes flavored with garlic. It is usually cut thin and eaten cold.

salm•on (**sam′** ən) A large saltwater and freshwater food fish with yellowish-pink flesh. It swims up large rivers in order to lay eggs.

saw (**sô**) A tool for cutting. It is made of a thin blade with sharp teeth on the edge.

sea gull (**sē′** gul′) A graceful, gray-and-white bird living on or near the sea.

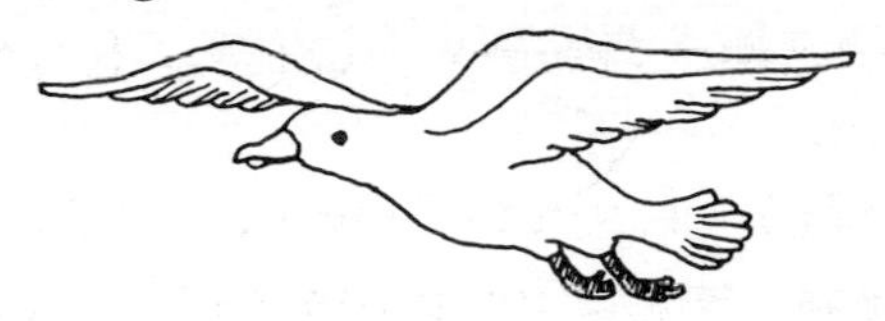

seal•ing (**sel′** ing) The hunting of seals.

search (**sėrch**) To try to find by looking.

sea•son•ing (**sē′** zn ing) Something added to food to give a better flavor. Salt, pepper, and herbs are seasonings.

sec•re•tar•y (**sek′** rə ter′ ē) A person who writes letters, keeps records, and so on.

ser•i•ous (**sir′** ē əs) Not fooling; sincere.

sew•age (**sü′** ij) The waste matter that passes through sewers.

shal•low (**shal′** ō) Not deep.

shark (**shärk**) A meat-eating fish that is usually large and lives in warm parts of the ocean.

shiv•er (**shiv′** ər) To shake with cold.

shrug (**shrug**) To raise the shoulders as a way to show not caring or not knowing.

sign (**sīn**) To write one's name.

skill (**skil**) An ability to do something very well.

solve (**solv**) To find the answer to; explain.

Span•ish (**span′** ish) Of Spain, its people, or their language.

spar•kle (**spär′** kəl) A little spark or flash.

spout (**spout**) A tube or lip by which liquid is poured.

spring (**spring**) Something, such as a wire, that can be pressed or stretched and will go back to its shape when it is released.

squat (**skwot**) Short and thick.

squirm (**skwėrm**) To show great embarrassment or confusion.

squirt (**skwėrt**) To force out liquid in a thin stream through a small opening.

stalk (**stôk**) A slender part of a plant that holds it up.

steam (**stēm**) An invisible gas. Water is changed into steam when it reaches the boiling point.

stern (**stėrn**) The rear part of a ship, boat, or airplane.

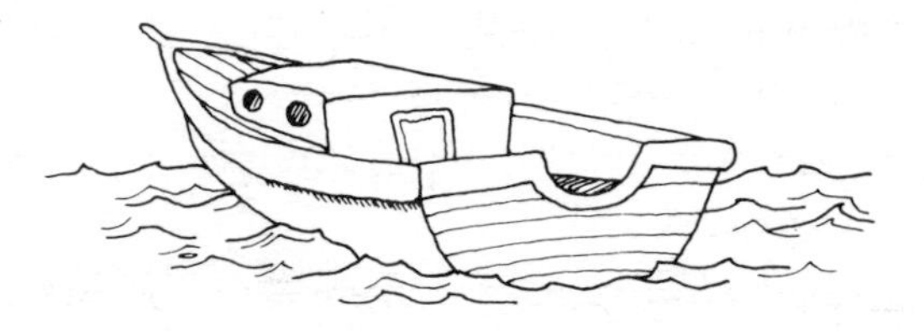

stilt (**stilt**) One of a pair of long poles, each with a foot rest high above the ground. Stilts can be used by children at play.

stone tab•let (**stōn tab′** lit) A thin, flat sheet made of stone and used to draw or write on. Long ago, people used stone tablets as we use sheets of paper.

a hat; **ā** age; **ä** father, far; **e** let; **ē** be; **ėr** term; **i** it; **ī** ice; **ng** long; **o** hot; **ō** open; **ô** order; **sh** she; **th** thin; **ᴛʜ** then; **u** cup; **ů** full; **ü** rule; **zh** measure; **ə** represents **a** in about, **e** in taken, **i** in pencil, **o** in lemon, **u** in circus.

store (**stôr**) To put away for use later.

stout (**stout**) Fat and large.

straight (**strāt**) 1. Without a bend; not crooked. 2. In the correct order or condition.

stran•ger (**strān'** jər) Someone not known, seen, or heard of before.

stub•born (**stub'** ərn) Fixed on having one's own way.

suck•er (**suk'** ər) An organ in some animals for sucking or holding fast by a sucking force.

sug•gest (səg **jest'**) To give out an idea as something to think about.

su•per (**sü'** pər) A part of a hive where honey is stored.

su•perb (sù **pėrb'**) Very fine; excellent.

sur•face (**sėr'** fis) The outside or top of a thing.

swamp (**swomp**) A wet, soft land; marsh.

swap (**swop**) To trade or exchange.

sym•bol (**sim'** bəl) Something that stands for something else.

T

tack•ling (**tak'** ling) The act of grabbing someone to stop movement.

talk down to (**tôk down tü**) To speak to in an I-am-better-than-you tone of voice.

tan•ge•rine (tan' jə **rēn'**) 1. Reddish-orange color. 2. A reddish-orange citrus fruit with a loose peel.

ta ta (**tä tä**) Good-bye; bye-bye.

that's the ticket (**ꝥHats ꝥHə tik'** it) That's just right; perfect.

three-quar•ters (thrē **kwôr'** tərz) Three of four equal parts.

thus (**ꝥHus**) In this way.

tink•er (**ting'** kər) A person who fixes pots, pans, and so on.

toad (**tōd**) A small, tailless animal that looks like a frog. Toads live most of the time on land rather than in water.

tool (**tül**) A saw, hammer, knife, or any instrument used in doing work.

touch•down (**tuch'** doun) A goal in football, for which six points are given.

tough (**tuf**) Rough; nasty.

tra•di•tion (trə **dish′** ən) Knowledge, beliefs, stories, and so on, handed down from parents to children.

trail (**trāl**) 1. A path through a wild area. 2. A track left by an animal, person, or thing.

trans•mit (tran **smit′**) To send out signals.

trum•pet (**trum′** pit) To make a sound like a trumpet.

trunk (**trungk**) An elephant's snout.

tsu•na•mi (tsü **nä′** mē) A huge ocean wave that usually causes great damage when it hits land. (Japanese)

tur•ret (**tėr′** it) A small tower that was used in the defense of a castle.

twip•per (**twi′** pər) To whistle or call like a bird.

U

un•eas•y (un **ē′** zē) Not comfortable.

u•su•al•ly (**yü′** zhü ə lē) Commonly; according to what is usual.

V

va•ca•tion (vā **kā′** shən) Freedom from school, business, or other duties.

vel•vet•y (**vel′** və tē) Smooth and soft like velvet cloth.

vil•lage (**vil′** ij) 1. The people of a small town. 2. A group of houses that makes up a small town.

W

wart hog (**wôrt′** hog) A wild hog of Africa that has two large tusks and large, wartlike growths on its face.

weird (**wird**) Odd; strange.

work some•thing out (**wėrk sum′** thing **out**) To figure out a way to do something.

Y

yak (**yak**) A long-haired ox of Tibet and central Asia. Yaks are raised for meat, milk, and hair and are used to carry things.

a hat; **ā** age; **ä** father, far; **e** let; **ē** be; **ėr** term; **i** it; **ī** ice; **ng** long; **o** hot; **ō** open; **ô** order; **sh** she; **th** thin; **ᴛʜ** then; **u** cup; **u̇** full; **ü** rule; **zh** measure; **ə** represents **a** in about, **e** in taken, **i** in pencil, **o** in lemon, **u** in circus.

Acknowledgments

(continued from page 3)

"Mayor Knucklebuckle Leaves a Key," Shirleyann Costigan. Page 300, "Kiwi," Shirleyann Costigan. Page 303, "Koala," Shirleyann Costigan.

L page 310, "Letters from Pliny," Daniel Veach. Page 318, "Three Funny Tricks," from *"Puzzles, Stunts, Brainteasers and Tricks" from Tell Me Why* by Arkady Leokum. © 1969 by Arkady Leokum. Page 318, "Reading, Writing, Arithmetic," from *A Twister of Twists, A Tangler of Tongues,* collected by Alvin Schwartz. Text copyright © 1972 by Alvin Schwartz. Reprinted by permission of J.B. Lippincott, Publishers. Page 322, adapted and reprinted from *Science Puzzles,* © 1975, by Laurence B. White, Jr., by permission of Children's Book Dept., Addison-Wesley Publishing Company, Inc. Page 323, adaptation of *The Crane Maiden* by Miyoko Matsutani, translated by Alvin Tresselt. Copyright © 1968 by Parents' Magazine Press. By permission of Parents' Magazine Press. Page 333, reprinted with permission of Macmillan Publishing Co., Inc. from *City Green* by Eleanor Schick. Copyright © 1974, Eleanor Schick.

The concept of *The Dictopedia* was suggested by Ellen Radtke.

Illustration Credits

Elizabeth A. Barry, designer   Trelawney N. Goodell, art editor

A pages 6–7, Eric Carle; pages 8–14, Lucinda McQueen; page 15, Jonathan L. Barkan; page 16, Jerry Pinkney; pages 17–18, Carol Nicklaus; pages 19–27, reprinted by permission of Coward, McCann & Geoghegan, Inc. from *"I Can't" Said the Ant* by Polly Cameron. Copyright © 1961 by Polly Cameron; page 28 (top), Debbie Sims; page 28 (bottom), Deidra Delano Stead; page 29, Ruth Brunner-Strosser; page 30 (left), The Metropolitan Museum of Art, Munsey Fund, 1932; pages 30–31, Judith DeLuca; page 31 (bottom), Jas. D. Easton, Inc.

B pages 34–35, Jonathan L. Barkan; page 36, Terri Huizinga; pages 37–41, John Wallner; page 42 (top), Erik Anderson; page 42 (bottom), Bob Barner; page 43, Marc Tolon Brown; pages 44–47, Guy Billout; pages 48–49, Les Morrill; pages 50–51, Peter Lippman; pages 52–53, Bob Barner; page 54 (bottom), Sal Murdocca; pages 55–56, Lynn Titleman; page 57, Sam Maitin.

C pages 59–60, Charles R. Brunner; page 61, Patrick Blackwell; pages 62–65, Arvis Stewart; page 66 (top), Kaufman © 1974 by The New York Times Company. Reprinted by permission; page 66 (bottom), Mark Kelley; page 67, Yoram Kahana, Peter Arnold, Inc.; pages 68–69, William Lillys; pages 70–71, Seymour Rosen; page 72, Los Angeles Times Photo, page 73, Terri Huizinga; page 74, Bob Krusling; pages 76–79, Leonard Lubin; pages 80–83, Reynold Ruffins; page 84, Carl Kock; page 85, David Frampton.

D page 86, Leslie Richmond; page 87, Judith DeLuca; pages 88–92, Tomie de Paola; page 93, Hilary Hayton; pages 94–97, Angela Adams; page 98, Victoria Chess; page 99 (top), Bob Barner; page 99 (bottom), Deidra Delano Stead; page 100, Jerome Kresch, Peter Arnold, Inc.; pages 101–102, Annie Gussman; page 103, Jeanette Kehl, Signature from The Martin Luther King, Jr. Collection, Department of Special Collections, Mugar Memorial Library, Boston University; pages 104–111, Quentin Blake.

E page 113, Bill Negron; page 114, John Wallner; page 115, Marie Zimmerman; pages 116–117, Amy Myers; pages 118–121, Jerry Pinkney; page 122, Martucci Studio; pages 123–125, Mark Desveaux; page 126 (top), Marc Tolon Brown; page 126 (bottom), Bob Barner; page 127, Frank Riley; pages 128–139, Marc Tolon Brown.

F page 141, Martucci Studio; page 142, Jane Nelson; pages 143–148, Terri Huizinga; page 149 (left), Jacqueline Adato; page 149 (right), David McPhail; pages 156–157, Judith DeLuca; pages 158–159, Stavros Cosmopoulos (from cover illustration for *New England Outdoors*); page 160, Andrew Sacks, Editorial Photocolor Archives; page 161, David Macaulay; pages 162–163, Western History Collections, University of Oklahoma Library; pages 164–167, Glen Rounds.

G pages 168–171, Pieter Bruegel d.A., *Kinderspiele*, Kunsthistorisches Museum, Vienna; pages 172–177, Alan Magee; pages 178–179, Bill Greer; page 180, Gunn Studio; pages 181–187, Mercer Mayer; pages 188–189, Sue B. Thompson; page 190 (top), Richard Hefter; page 190 (bottom), Bob Barner; page 191 (bottom), Bob Barner; pages 192–194, Paul Goble.

H page 196 (left), Bob Barner; page 196 (right), Martucci Studio; page 197, Walter Einsel (sculpture); page 197, Kevin Callahan; pages 198–203, Rick Brown; page 204, Sal Murdocca; page 205, Lois Basilio; pages 206–214, Jerry Pinkney; page 215, Bob Dole; page 216, Deidra Delano Stead; pages 218–221 (left), Charles Freeman; page 221 (right), Ron Austing, Bruce Coleman Inc.

I page 222, Frank Bozzo; pages 223–225, Reynold Ruffins; pages 226–230, Christa Kieffer; pages 231–245, Patrick O. Chapin; pages 246–248, third-grade students, Bridge School, Lexington, Massachusetts. Barbara Bole, art specialist; page 249, Bill Finch, Stock, Boston, Inc. (photograph).

J page 250, Bob Barner; page 251, Marc Tolon Brown; pages 252–253, The Fairchild Syndicate; page 255 (left), Mikimoto (America) Co., Ltd; page 255 (right), The Fairchild Syndicate; pages 256–265, Ruth Brunner-Strosser; page 266, Deidra Delano Stead; page 267, Bill Charmatz; pages 268–272, Allen Davis; page 273, Tivi Etook; pages 274–275, Lionel Kalish.

K page 276, Manfred Kage, Peter Arnold, Inc.; pages 277–278, Bill Morrison; page 277, Interpress-Austral, Photo Trends; page 278, Australian Information Service; pages 279–289, John Keely; pages 290–291, Bill Morrison; page 290, Arthur Ambler, National Audubon Society Collection, Photo Researchers, Inc.; page 293, Terri Huizinga; pages 294–298, Jon McIntosh; page 299 (top), Bob Barner; page 299 (bottom), Joan Paley; page 300, Van Nostrand, National Audubon Society Collection, Photo Researchers, Inc.; page 301, Bill Morrison; page 302, Victoria Chess; pages 303-304, Bill Morrison; page 304, Grant-Thompson, Annan Photo Features.

L page 305, Martucci Studio; page 306, Jerry Zimmerman; page 307, Richard Spencer; pages 308–309, Vincenzo Carcavallo. Photographs from *The Town of Hercules: A Buried Treasure Trove* by Joseph Jay Deiss. © 1974. Reprinted by permission of Houghton Mifflin Company; pages 310–313, Charles Shaw; pages 314–317, Superintendent of Antiquities, Naples. Photographs from *The Town of Hercules: A Buried Treasure Trove* by Joseph Jay Deiss. © 1974. Reprinted by permission of Houghton Mifflin Company; page 318–319 (top), third-grade students, Bridge School, Lexington, Massachusetts. Barbara Bole, art specialist; page 319 (bottom), from *A Very Young Dancer,* by Jill Krementz. Copyright © 1976 by Jill Krementz. Reprinted by permission of Alfred A. Knopf, Inc.; pages 320–321, The Bettmann Archive, Inc.; page 322, Marc Tolon Brown from *Science Puzzles* © 1975, by permission of Addison-Wesley Publishing Company, Inc.; pages 323–332, Kinuko Craft; page 333, Jacqueline Adato.

Our thanks to Bill Wall for *bathtub and hamburger.*
Mechanical art, Ann Lampton Curtis, Nini Evans, Joe Durkin.